INDUSTRIAL COST CONTROLS

INDUSTRIAL
COST CONTROLS

Frank C. Wilson, P. E.

Prentice-Hall, Inc.   **Englewood Cliffs, N. J.**

PRENTICE-HALL INTERNATIONAL, INC., *London*
PRENTICE-HALL OF AUSTRALIA, PTY. LTD., *Sydney*
PRENTICE-HALL OF CANADA, LTD., *Toronto*
PRENTICE-HALL OF INDIA PRIVATE LTD., *New Delhi*
PRENTICE-HALL OF JAPAN, INC., *Tokyo*

© 1971, BY

PRENTICE-HALL, INC.
ENGLEWOOD CLIFFS, N. J.

LIBRARY OF CONGRESS
CATALOG CARD NO.: 75-132039

PRINTED IN THE UNITED STATES OF AMERICA
ISBN—0-13-459453-3
B & P

DEDICATION

To my family
Anne, Lynn and Chip

and

with grateful appreciation to Mrs. Bradley Edmond-son, my secretary; Mr. McCoy Griffin, Manager of Cost Accounting, West Point Pepperell, for mathe-matical verification; Mr. Ronald R. Z. Jones, Honeywell EDP for data processing programs; and Mrs. Malcolm Lathem for final proofing of the text.

ACKNOWLEDGMENTS

I wish to express my sincere thanks to

Consulting Editor

Professor William W. Hines, Ph.D.
Georgia Institute of Technology
School of Systems & Industrial Engineering
Atlanta, Georgia

Reading Editors

John W. Davis, C.P.A.
Controller
Greenwood Mills
Greenwood, South Carolina

John Fyfe, R.I.A.
Controller
Iroqois Chemicals Limited
Cornwall, Ontario, Canada

C. O. Ericson
Consulting Engineer
The Swedish Sales Institute
Stockholm, Sweden

ABOUT
THE
AUTHOR

Mr. Frank C. Wilson is a Registered Professional Engineer and specialized management consultant serving leading U. S. and international carpet, chemical, textile, and related industries. He is a graduate of Auburn University, the Graduate School of the Georgia Institute of Technology, and has studied at New York University. He has been elected for honorary societies in research—the Society of Sigma Xi and industrial engineering—Alpha Phi Mu.

Mr. Wilson specializes in the fields of marketing, industrial planning, and management control. His publications have appeared in significant North American and European journals. He has been selected to speak and lead seminars in the U. S., Canada, and Europe.

In addition to over twenty years of business and management experience, he has had teaching assignments at the Georgia Institute of Technology. Mr. Wilson is a member of several professional, industrial, and honorary groups including the National Association of Accountants, National Association of Professional Engineers, American Marketing Association, American Institute of Industrial Engineers, and others.

The Benefits
Offered by This Book

This book was sparked by the accelerated velocity and complexity of business change. Costs are constantly rising and yet, consumer prices are difficult to increase. Though the technology explosion requires specialization, there is an increasing need for understanding the total business—the interrelation of one department to another.

An integrated system of market forecast, engineered costs, calculated budgets, and target prices is the life blood through which effective control of business is realized. Management information is no longer simply another accounting function. Effective business control is based on a total management system—meaning, decisions are based on a synthesis of cost, financial and sales data.

The techniques illustrated in this book enable the reader to follow the development of a management information system from forecast through manufacturing, distribution and sales to control reports. A model system is used from data collection to output reports. This permits the implementation of a similar system for any business, whether its processes include batch processing, machine hours, or continuous processes.

Effective operational and financial managers must understand their cost calculation and control systems. The comprehension of the methods utilized and how they respond to business situations are possibly more important than theoretical accuracy. This book will help the reader understand cost calculations control reports and show him how decisions influence performance and business results. It permits the efficient use of time to increase knowledge of effective total management methods in both depth and scope.

This indispensable tool helps the treasurer, controller and cost accountant gain a better perspective of the total business and the effect of cost and financial information on management decisions. And it gives a spectrum of managers—business, division, plant, marketing, product, distribution, sales and financial—useful, lasting, and constructive industrial planning and control applications.

Future successful businesses will be based on systematic planning and control. This book develops a model system to accomplish this objective. Everyone who utilizes or supplies management information—industrial engineers, accountants, systems analysts and others—will find this book a guide to designing and installing their own system.

The author concentrates on results—profit forecasting, product evaluations, and pricing decisions—rather than accounting transactions and entries. Taking the approach that direct costing, absorption costing, and marginal income are merely variations in information analysis, the author develops management information and control techniques extracting the best features of these and other methods.

The examples, techniques and methods are based on the author's consulting, marketing and management experience of over twenty years. There is no need for the reader to find out the hard way, through erroneous decisions and actions. The author points out many of the pitfalls to avoid in the firm, division or plant.

This book is organized around the marketing concept and acceptable accounting practice. A checklist for industrial planning is included along with a special section on international marketing. Automated data processing applications and output reports are displayed which the reader will want to use in his business. Examples include quantity discount pricing using a Canadian industry situation, pricing by product line and trade channel, control reports for the three levels of supervision—department, plant and division or firm—forecasting, production and inventory control reports. Special attention is given to pricing new products for maximum return. In addition, the reader is shown how to extend the life cycle and contribution of products in a declining market.

The author is well aware that prices may be set in the competitive marketplace. But by knowing the real cost, the reader can select from the market those *few* products, styles, or items which will contribute the most to return on investment. This book shows how to determine cost and analyze sales to select the best products, volumes and channels of distribution.

As our industrial operations become larger and more complex, business managers —all who provide or use management information, and those who make decisions— must move into the uncertain future with a feeling of security and a better understanding of the total firm and their place in it. This book develops a model system of forecasting, business planning, cost calculation, and management control. Applicable to most industrial operations and businesses, the techniques described will help managers develop better analytical information, reduce the timing of decisions, and improve management judgment . . . as the markets, the technology, the competition, and people continually change.

I sincerely believe that this book will help financial men and business managers make better decisions, increase income and produce new streams of earnings. It will help the reader obtain and evaluate information and thus reduce the range of decision error. It will contribute to the foundation of knowledge and understanding—the seedbed of intelligent business decisions—with the result that options are sharpened and the right action is more apt to be executed at the right time. Or, to put it another way, the advice in this book can help businessmen move into the uncertain future with less frustration.

Frank C. Wilson, P.E.

What This Book
Will Do for You

- A good market forecast is the foundation for effective business planning and control. Chapter One explains the techniques, pitfalls, advantages and applications of trend analysis for long-range forecast; exponential smoothing for production planning and inventory control; multiple regression for market research and diffusion indexes for turns in business conditions.

- Managers must ask the right questions. Chapter Two includes a checklist of key questions for each area of the business.

- Control of materials (waste) may be the most important for many firms. Chapter Three tells you how to calculate engineered standards, calculate and control cost.

- Labor cost is important in most every industry. In Chapter Four, you will learn how to determine and control these costs, particularly the fast increasing labor benefits.

- Manufacturing expenses—fuel, supplies, salaries—must be separated into variable and fixed categories. Chapter Five explains how to separate, budget, cost and control these items on an analytical, engineered basis.

- Chapter Six illustrates the use of machine hours for calculating manufacturing expenses. The disadvantages of other methods are explored.

- Efficient distribution cost is essential in the seventies. Chapter Seven points out how to develop and control distribution cost. A Canadian industry example is illustrated.

- Effective financial results—profits (or contribution)—must be related to investment. Chapter Eight will show you how to do this by product or trade channel.

- Prices may be set by markets and competition. Yet, with sound cost information and target prices, effective managers can analyze sales and select from the market those products, customers, and trade channels which will contribute significantly to results. You can determine which items to delete while maintaining a complete range of products (see Chapter Nine). Special sections include international market pricing, new product decisions, and exploiting the product life cycle in declining markets.

• Management is decisions and actions. Chapter Ten displays reports and control methods to evaluate the expected results of potential decisions—volumes, prices, trade channels . . . and others.

HOW THIS BOOK IS ORGANIZED . . . HOW TO USE IT

This book is organized to use your time effectively . . . to systematically develop a business planning and control system in sufficient detail so you can plan and implement similar techniques and methods in your firm. Theoretically sound and based on accepted accounting practice, the methods, examples and text concentrate on getting things done in your firm, your department, or your business.

In each chapter, every expense or budget is developed, costs calculated and control report displayed. Rather than jump from one industry example to another, this book follows one example from data collection, calculation to output reports. You can adapt these methods to your firm—step by step. Certain methods and techniques are recommended for various situations. The pitfalls and advantages of others are explored so you can make the best decision for your firm.

Table of Contents

13

Chapter Two—continued

Manufacturing Process—41 · Organization and Responsibilities—41 · Typical Products, Parts, or Items—42 · Plant Layout and Floor Space Utilization—43 · Standard Purchased Material Prices—43 · List of Machinery and Replacement Values—46 · Salary Budgets—47 · Hourly Labor Complement—48 · Specification Sheets—49 · Cost Calculation Methods—49 · Systematic Planning—51

CHAPTER THREE

Initial Raw Materials—55 · Material Loss Standards—62 · Material Control—65 · Calculations of Gains (or Losses)—67 · Multipliers for Cost Calculation—69 · Cost of Sales—71

CHAPTER SIX

Cost Sheet Design—111 · Calculation of Manufacturing Costs—113 · Defining Cost Centers—117 · Idle Capacity Costs—117 · Costs of Quality—121 · Control of Quality Cost—124

⌇⌇⌇⌇⌇⌇⌇⌇⌇⌇ *Illustrations in Chapter Six* ⌇⌇⌇⌇⌇⌇⌇⌇⌇

CHAPTER SEVEN

Channels of Distribution—127 · Fixed Distribution Staff—129 · Warehouse Location—129 · Warehouse Cost—132 · Transportation Cost—132 · Distribution Services Expense—138 · Calculation of Distribution Cost—140

⌇⌇⌇⌇⌇⌇⌇⌇⌇ *Illustrations in Chapter Seven* ⌇⌇⌇⌇⌇⌇⌇⌇⌇

CHAPTER EIGHT

Budget Specification Sheet—143 · Budget Control—145 · Summary of Ex-

Chapter Eight—continued

Illustrations in Chapter Eight

CHAPTER NINE

Illustrations in Chapter Nine

CHAPTER TEN

Chapter Ten—continued

Management Control Statement—183 • Cash Flow—186 • Sales and Profit Forecasting—186 • Breakeven Point Calculation—187 • Forecasting Reduced Operations—190 • Forecasting Increased Operations—191 • Sales Price Change—192 • A Business Situation—195 • Product Mix Change—195 • Channel of Distribution Change—198 • Other Profit Forecast—198 • People and Communications—199

Illustrations in Chapter Ten

INDUSTRIAL COST CONTROLS

CHAPTER ONE

Forecasting for Industrial Planning

The first step in establishing a business model control system is the development of market information and statistics—*Which present markets have the best long-range potential?* and *What new products should be evaluated for future development?* The techniques of business forecasting give management an opportunity to obtain more analytical information and to reduce the range of decision error in determining expense mark-ups, profit forecasts, and capacity evaluations for capital expenditures.

Primarily, managers have five different needs in the forecasting markets:

(1) Routine production scheduling and inventory control.
(2) Long-range market forecasting for planning capacity and capital expenditures.
(3) Basic market research to seek out the causes of present and future demand.
(4) Prediction of short-run "turns" in the economy.
(5) Development of a strategy to capture an optimum share of the market through the best economic balance of prices, products, quality, markets, advertising, sales effort, and service.

The objective in this chapter is to present general forecasting techniques and the pitfalls and advantages of certain methods. The step-by-step procedures are well documented in statistical texts and other publications.

Exponential Smoothing for Short-Range Forecasting

Exponential smoothing is most useful for routine forecasting for production and inventory control. Though the mathematics can be complex, it is simply a different kind of weighted average. This technique is similar to zeroing-in a rifle. A forecast is made and continually adjusted for the error.

As an example, assume a stockkeeping item has had or is expected to have sales of 1,000 units per week, month, or other time interval. This, then, becomes the initial current average.

In order to obtain a forecast for the next time period, this initial current average is adjusted for the seasonal variation. Though the average sales may be 1,000 per time period, historical data may indicate that 1,200 units will be sold in the next period, 1,500 in the following period, and so on. This gives a seasonal variation of 1.20 and 1.50. Of course, some periods will be less than 1.00, for the total monthly seasonal factors for a year must total 12.00.

A forecast for the next period may be obtained by:

Initial Current Average $\times$ Seasonal Factor
(1,000 $\times$ 1.20) = 1,200 Units

This forecast is then compared with actual sales for the next period, say 1,300 units. The forecast error is:

Actual Sales $-$ Forecast Sales $=$ Error
(1,300 $-$ 1,200) $= +$ 100

This error is then adjusted with a *smoothing constant*. This constant varies, depending on the degree of variation in actual sales. It can be determined by statistical processes involving the comparison of the forecast error for various constants tested. Frequently, for large volume sales with reasonable variation, a constant of 0.10 is useful. For more erratic data, factors of 0.20 or 0.30 may give a more accurate forecast. In this example, a smoothing constant of 0.20 is assumed.

Now, the new current average is:

Initial Current Average $+$ Constant $\times$ Error $=$ New Current Average
1,000 $+$ (0.20 $\times$ +100) $=$ 1,020

The process is continued from time period to time period. Even with a poor initial current average, a good forecast can be obtained in a few periods due to the self-correction feature of exponential smoothing.

By using a constant of 0.20, this portion of the error is considered to be real. The remainder (0.80) of the error is a result of random, non-recurring factors. Generally, a chart of a series of forecasts versus actual sales using exponential smoothing will follow the pattern shown in Figure 1-1.

For perfectly random sales, the forecast and actual sales lines will cross. In most real data of stockkeeping items, a degree of systematic influence will be present from time to time.

More sophisticated exponential systems include trend components and more complex equations. For routine sales forecasting and production control, trend components can be misleading. Often, although the entire product line may be trending up or down, an individual stockkeeping item which is a size, color, or part may not be following the trend. In addition, for individual items, this component may change direc-

Forecast Data
Smoothing Constant = 0.20

Period	Current Average	Seasonal Factor	Forecast Sales	Actual Sales	Error	Current Average Adjustment
1	1,000	1.20	1,200	1,300	+ 100	+ 20
2	1,020	1.30	1,326	1,526	+ 200	+ 40
3	1,060	1.20	1,272	1,372	+ 100	+ 20
4	1,080	1.10	1,188	1,238	+ 50	+ 10
5	1,090	1.00	1,090	1,040	- 50	- 10
6	1,080	0.90	972	1,072	+ 100	+ 20
7	1,100	0.80	880	800	- 80	- 16
8	1,084	0.90	976	1,016	+ 40	+ 8
9	1,092	1.00	1,092			

FIGURE 1-1
EXPONENTIAL SMOOTHING FORECAST

tion from time to time. This trend component, then, can give an erroneous forecast, particularly when more distant forecasts are being prepared.

For exponential smoothing to be successful, a reasonable degree of randomness in sales statistics is required. This requirement is normally met with consumer items covering a significant number of customers. It is not met when large orders are received from a few customers.

The time interval for updating forecasts is important. A weekly or biweekly update is most helpful for dynamic scheduling. Sometimes, with erratic data, a monthly forecast is more accurate to smooth out non-systematic week-to-week variation. For monthly forecasts, four-week time intervals (13 forecasts per year) are best. Four-week intervals help to give nearer the same number of selling days per period and can be converted easily to get a weekly average.

From a computer standpoint, exponential smoothing permits rapid updating with a minimum of data stored in computer records. The forecast and error components can be utilized to calculate reorder points, standard inventory quantities, and production required for given lead times and customer service levels.

A key to effective production and inventory control is the utilization of the error component. Some programs include automatic adjustment for large errors. In some cases this will result in a better forecast. However, if the large error is due to a non-systematic influence, such as an error in the data or large contract order, the forecast will be incorrect and will result in the production of excess or inadequate inventory.

For effective application, computer programs must be developed to print out exception reports of error conditions for manual review based on the significance of the error. Typical forecasts and exception reports are shown in Figures 1-2, 1-3, 1-4, and 1-5.

Exception reports must include methods of correction and adjustment. As an example, an advertising program may be planned on selected products or items. This influence will cause an unforecasted surge in demand. Manual adjustments must be made in the exponential forecast to reflect this potential demand.

The use of exponential smoothing for production and inventory control can improve customer service, reduce inventories, and improve management short-run decisions. These data can be used to plan production to achieve stable employment. They provide an analytical basis for minimizing total cost using factors of overtime cost, layoff cost, out-of-stock conditions, inventory, storage cost, and other related expenses.

Trend Analysis for Long-Range Forecasting

Trend analysis is a technique for long-range forecasting. More complex mathematical models include seasonal and cyclical variation. The general equation is:

$$Y_i = T_i \times S_i \times C_i \times E_i$$

where Y_i = Forecast of shipments in the i'th time period,
T_i = Trend component,
S_i = Seasonal component,
C_i = Cyclical component,
and E_i = Error component.

DIVISION: AUTOMOTIVE　　　　　　　　　　　　　　　　　　PLANT: ATLANTA

	PRODUCT NUMBER	SIZE CODE	COLOR CODE	LAST YEAR AVERAGE	PERIOD 1	PERIOD 2	PERIOD 3	PERIOD 4	PERIOD 5	PERIOD 6	PERIOD 7	NEW FORECAST
ACTUAL ORDERS	C-300	120	1010	478	499	615	423	337	187	453	662	456
FORECAST					527	483	454	417	445	386	372	
ERROR					28-	132	31-	80-	258-	67	290	
AVERAGE					439	478	469	445	368	388	475	
ERROR FACTOR					1.10	.15	1.70	2.15	2.50	1.45	.05	
ACTUAL ORDERS	C-500	120	1020	1293	1380	1692	460	1261	1376	500	1042	975
FORECAST					1385	1290	1228	946	1157	1283	948	
ERROR					5-	402	768-	315	219	783-	94	
AVERAGE					1173	1293	1063	1157	1222	988	1016	
ERROR FACTOR					.45	1.55	1.65	1.25	.45	1.20	2.10	
ACTUAL ORDERS	C-500	120	1030	148	128	191	66	91	279	234	200	179
FORECAST					177	150	141	112	120	164	170	
ERROR					49-	41	75-	21-	159	70	30	
AVERAGE					136	148	126	120	156	177	186	
ERROR FACTOR					2.25	2.90	2.60	2.80	.75	2.35	2.25	
ACTUAL ORDERS	C-500	120	1060	125	192	151	75	318	228	319	106	166
FORECAST					113	131	119	100	142	158	189	
ERROR					79	20	44-	218	86	161	83-	
AVERAGE					119	125	112	142	150	197	173	
ERROR FACTOR					1.55	1.65	1.70	2.80	4.00	4.15	2.85	
ACTUAL ORDERS	C-500	120	1090	294	186	353	296	31	176	129	180	118
FORECAST					413	310	279	266	229	225	93	
ERROR					227-	43	17	235-	53-	96-	87	
AVERAGE					282	294	299	229	214	97	123	
ERROR FACTOR					2.35	2.35	1.05	2.80	3.95	3.60	2.85	

FIGURE 1-2
DETAIL FORECAST PRINT-OUT

DIVISION: AUTOMOTIVE

DATE: XX-XX-XX

PLANT: ATLANTA

	PRODUCT NUMBER	SIZE CODE	COLOR CODE	LAST YEAR AVERAGE	PERIOD 1	PERIOD 2	PERIOD 3	PERIOD 4	PERIOD 5	PERIOD 6	PERIOD 7	NEW FORECAST
ACTUAL ORDERS	C-500	120	1060	125	192	151	75	318	228	319	106	166
FORECAST					113	131	119	100	142	158	189	
ERROR					79	20	44-	218	86	161	83-	
AVERAGE					119	125	112	142	150	197	173	
ERROR FACTOR					1.55	1.65	1.70	2.80	4.00	4.15	2.85	
ACTUAL ORDERS	C-500	120	1090	294	186	353	296	31	176	129	180	118
FORECAST					413	310	279	266	229	225	93	
ERROR					227-	43	17	235-	53-	96-	87	
AVERAGE					282	294	299	229	214	97	123	
ERROR FACTOR					2.35	2.35	1.05	2.80	3.95	3.60	2.85	

ERROR FACTOR IS

CUT-OF-CONTROL

FIGURE 1-3

EXCEPTION REPORT OF FORECAST DATA

DIVISION: AUTOMOTIVE　　　　　　　　　　　DATE: XX-XX-XX　　　　　　　　　　PLANT: ATLANTA

PRODUCT NUMBER	SIZE CODE	COLOR CODE	WEEKS OF LEAD TIME	SERVICE LEVEL	FINISHED INVENTORY	UNFILLED ORDERS	WORK-IN PROCESS	NET AVAILABLE	FORECAST 12 WEEKS	REORDER POINT	QUANTITY TO SCHEDULE
					----------STOCK STATUS - UNITS----------						
					+	-	+	=			
C-420	120	2010	4	90	1,000	0	0	1,000	3,600	2,000	2,200
C-900	120	2520	2	90	1,000	0	500	1,500	2,400	1,000	0

FIGURE 1-4

PRODUCTION PLANNING AND SCHEDULING INFORMATION

DIVISION: AUTOMOTIVE　　　　　　　　　　　DATE: XX-XX-XX　　　　　　　　　　PLANT: ATLANTA

PRODUCT NUMBER	SIZE CODE	COLOR CODE	PLANNED INVENTORY UNITS	PLANNED INVENTORY $	ACTUAL INVENTORY UNITS	ACTUAL INVENTORY $	OVERSTOCKED UNITS	OVERSTOCKED $	UNDERSTOCKED UNITS	UNDERSTOCKED $	SERVICE LEVEL STANDARD	SERVICE LEVEL ACTUAL	OUT-OF-CONTROL
C-500	120	1970	2,000	6,000	3,000	9,000	500	1,500	-	-	90	91	OVERSTOCKED
C-600	150	1860	4,000	16,000	1,000	4,000	-	-	1,000	4,000	85	75	SERVICE LEVEL

FIGURE 1-5

INVENTORY CONTROL INFORMATION

A typical example of a linear trend forecast is shown in Figure 1-6. This example includes prediction limits for upper and lower limits based on given statistical calculations. In this one, the limits are based on a 0.95 probability of occurrence.

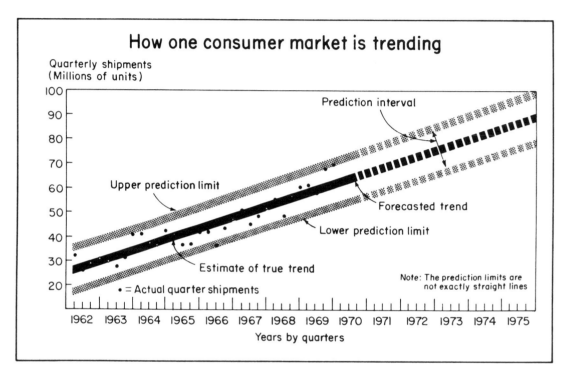

FIGURE 1-6
LINEAR TREND PROJECTION

There are both simple and complex statistical methods of calculating a trend equation. Frequently, the simple approaches result in equally as good a forecast as the more complex techniques of determining an equation. In many cases, time series data may require a non-linear equation for the best results.

In forecasting for time series where the seasonal component expands as the trend increases (consumer goods), use the multiplicative model shown above. Others may require the same model with additive components.

For a long-range, five to ten years, annual forecast, a seasonal forecast component is not normally required. Even when these types of forecasts are for quarterly or other time intervals, the validity of a seasonal adjustment is questionable for any given year.

Much study has been devoted to cyclical analysis. Some evidence of cyclical variations does exist in some time series sales data. In many cases, the cyclical component has lost its significance as a reult of government intervention in the economy and in international events.

For forecasts involving dollars, long-range forecasts should be developed for real demand in constant dollars. Inflationary trends can often result in misleading forecasts, particularly if dollars and average expected prices are used to convert to a long-range forecast of units to be sold.

In most industries, long-range forecasts must be separated between domestic shipments, exports, and imports. Other subdivisions may be helpful to develop a meaningful estimate for management decisions for capital expenditures and plant construction.

Long-range total industry forecasts are important. Yet, plants must be constructed to produce specific items. For good profit forecasts and financial planning, cost must be developed for typical items. These should not be based on total dollars or percentages. Specific items, prices, and costs are required for management to maintain control and determine the reasons for attainment or non-attainment of objectives.

A key to long-range forecasts is the selection of the time period for analysis. Forecasts based on historical data assume that conditions which existed in the past will exist in the future. An analysis of data, say for the past ten years in a growth economy, may give one forecast ten years in the future, whereas an analysis of the past 15 years may give a significantly different forecast. Management must be careful to understand the basis for any long-range forecast, for markets do not always expand. In the long run, almost any market can be expected to decline at certain points in time even though the trend may be toward growth.

In addition, actual economic conditions for any given year may vary from the trend forecast. In some cases this could be extremely important, particularly when a new plant involving a large capital expenditure comes into production in a declining year. Often it seems that managers are concerned only with growth trends, and this optimism is good. Yet managers must insist that long-range forecasts be made of declining markets in order to plan to get out of a particular market before products and plants in this declining market begin to erode the profits.

Multiple Regression Analysis for Basic Demand Analysis

Multiple regression analysis involves determining the constants for a linear relationship of several variables and their effect on the demand for a product such as carpets, automobiles, and others.

The general equation is:

$$Y_i = C + c_1X_1 + c_2X_2 + c_3X_3 \ldots c_kX_k + E_i$$

where
Y_i = Forecast of the dependent variable, such as carpets,

C = Constant,

c = Coefficient,

X_k = Independent variables,

and E_i = Error component.

Many variables may be analyzed with the aid of computers. In the case of a home or office furnishing product, these may be:

X_1 = New housing starts,
X_2 = Discretionary income per household,
X_3 = Commercial construction of offices and
          other public buildings,
X_4 = Apartment construction,
X_5 = School construction,
X_6 = Mobile home construction,
X_7 = Competing product sales,
and X_8 = Shipments "i" years earlier.

Though a hundred or more variables may be tested, fewer than five or ten may be finally selected to give a prediction with reasonable accuracy.

The variable X_7 may indicate the potential available which is now being filled by competing products. Market research must always seek out those areas of potential demand for products in addition to those included in historical data.

Variable X_8 may be an indication of replacement demand for items which have an estimated useful life. These include most consumer items—automobiles, appliances, home furnishings, clothing, and such products.

In multiple regression analysis, our market research people sometimes select a very extensive list of hundreds of variables to be analyzed. Managers must insist that all variables selected for analysis and inclusion in multiple regression models have a logical cause and effect relationship.

Similarly, variables selected for analysis must be sensitive and applicable to the particular product. Such series as Gross National Product and Disposal Personal Income are interesting and helpful for total industry predictions. For individual products, the level of aggregation may be too high for meaningful predictions. As an example, a consumer product sales dollars may range around 0.20 percent of Disposal Personal Income. In this case, even a small change in the statistic would result in a significant variation in the product forecast.

Though multiple regression analysis is a good tool for studying past data, it is suspect for future predictions. The difficulty lies in obtaining leading variables which can be forecasted with a reasonable degree of accuracy.

Diffusion Index for Forecasting
Short-Run Turns in the Economy

Diffusion indexes offer an opportunity to predict changes in economic conditions in advance of an up-turn or down-turn. Extensive work for total industry indexes has been done by the National Industrial Conference Board. A typical diffusion index chart is shown in Figure 1-7.

Short-term changes in economic conditions are important as a supplement to exponential smoothing for forecasts to be utilized in production and inventory control. A system can be functioning smoothly; then a sudden down-turn occurs throughout the industry. In this case, all of the excess production for the lower sales requirements will enter into inventory, causing an overstocked condition. Similar situations can occur in

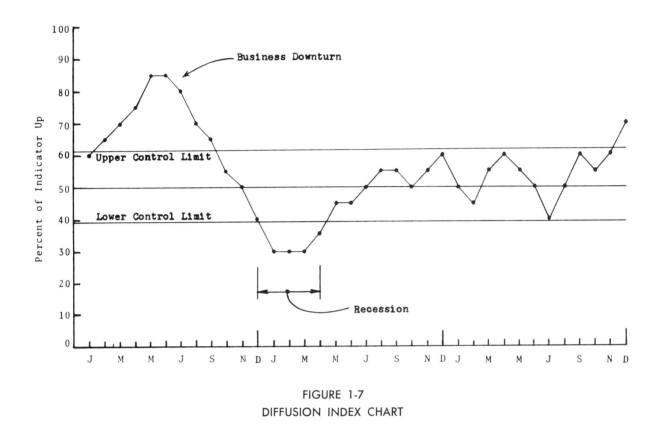

FIGURE 1-7
DIFFUSION INDEX CHART

consumer goods items when weather, political conditions, or some other factor disturbs normal purchases.

A diffusion index involves the selection of leading indicators such as new housing starts, automobile production, interest rates, and others. The percent of indicators advancing or declining may be an indicator of future business conditions. Control limits, which may indicate a significant change, can be estimated. These limits may be of questionable validity in real situations.

Here, as with multiple regression analysis, the difficulty is in locating leading indicators for a particular industry for which data are available far enough in advance to predict a change and permit action by management.

Other Forecasting Techniques

There are a number of other techniques available to obtain additional knowledge of the market. These include surveys, ratios, and others. Each has a specialized use and should be reviewed for certain applications.

Extensive work has been done in developing industrial dynamics or systems models with feedback characteristics for total industries. These techniques present an exciting opportunity to expand the field of knowledge for total industries, and possibly for selected products.

Mathematical simulation is an aid in cutting risk in management decisions. Simulation is a method, often mathematical, involving the creation of a model for business or other situations. Its application helps predict the results for a given set of conditions. The model can be manipulated for a variety of conditions and alternatives. Industrial dynamics system studies are conducted with simulation, as are flow systems including production, inventory, and customer service.

Simulation techniques will not make decisions for managers. They will provide the basis for experimentation to the decision makers. The results of simulation experiments can minimize the dangers of making wrong decisions. Simulation models are not new. Military strategists have long used simulation techniques to evaluate alternative situations in battle problems and techniques of war games. Executive business simulation "games" involve competitive strategies, effect of price changes, and variation in potential demand.

Simulation models are categorized by degree of abstraction. An example of a non-abstract, but real simulation, is a wear test. Like other fatigue tests, it compresses time, making a minute equal to a day, a week, or a month.

In much the same way, a miniature plane in a wind tunnel simulates flight conditions and a pilot plant simulates full scale production. Likewise, managers of many businesses simulate business conditions to test the effect of changes in competition, inventories, and markets. A symbolic model involving probability concepts is often utilized. Such models allow events to occur randomly according to assigned probabilities.

Managers must make good use of models of process conditions and markets to simulate future results. They need to strive to develop information on results in advance of decision making. Then they should compare actual results to expected results as our decisions are implemented. Effective managers require an understanding of simulation systems including demand, inventory, and production variations.

Utilization of Forecast Data

Management must be familiar with estimated expected demand in order to establish goals and volumes for standard costs and prices. (This will be illustrated in the following chapters.) Standard cost must reflect long-run cost by method of distribution in a good, controlled business. Unit profit margins based on standard costs and prices should be related to long-range objectives of the organization. These may be disjointed from year-to-year accounting and expense budgets. Standard cost must be changed as time and conditions change the basic components of raw material, manufacturing expenses, and others.

Management must set an objective or target and develop its standard costs and budgets to attain this target. A key factor is in differentiating the real cost for diversified products, processes, and channels of distribution. Linear programming and other mathematical techniques are opportunities to improve management decisions. These methods are valid only when they are based on real cost data.

Regardless of the statistics or mathematical techniques utilized, the results must be supplemented with management judgment and knowledge of the markets in the final business plan. The successful manager develops and maintains a total business plan including research and product development, manufacturing, engineering, sales, and marketing. The first step is developing an objective, then preparing a coordinated business plan to achieve the objective. There are no isolated decisions. Business cannot be separated into compartments, with assigned responsibilities. All departments must be "on the same drive shaft" if a business is to achieve its maximum potential.

SUMMARY

Effective management is based on a factual approach to business judgment. This can be achieved through analysis of information, allocation of resources, decisions, and actions.

The first step is establishing a business objective and market strategy based on market demand. Forecasts of market potential may be based on exponential smoothing, trend analysis, multiple regression, diffusion indexes, and other statistical techniques. Linear programming, simulation, and related mathematical techniques guide managers in optimizing resources and maximizing financial results.

Decision rules and exception reports must be developed to aid managers to sort out and concentrate on the few areas which will significantly contribute to higher profits.

The successful manager must develop and maintain a total business plan including research, product development, manufacturing, sales, marketing, and administration. Mathematical data must be evaluated with management judgment and knowledge of the markets.

The business plan should be based on engineered standards, budgets, and expected cost of a good, controlled business by channel of distribution. Last year's average costs are suspect. The long-range plan may be disjointed from year-to-year business results.

The following chapters of this book explain how market objectives can be translated into a total business plan for management decisions, actions, and control.

CHAPTER TWO

Planning a Control System

Planning offers both opportunities and challenges to improve performance and organize the future. It permits managers to move into the uncertain years ahead with a feeling of security. Improvements do not occur by chance. They must be planned and managed.

Planning is not an attempt to eliminate risk. It is an attempt to *define* risk and take the right risk rather than plunge into the uncertain future on a hunch, hearsay, or experience. It does not restrict the individual manager's initiative, judgment, or responsibility. It does provide a basis for decisions and actions.

Planning involves measurement. Once a decision is made, the results must be measured as related to the target.

Planning may, in the end, be intuitive. Yet, it is a factual, systematic approach to business judgment. It is the dynamic process of management setting objectives and revising goals as time and conditions change.

The requirements for planning are:

(a) Defining alternative courses of action and risk.
(b) Making decisions and taking actions.
(c) Measuring results and revising objectives.

The management control system developed in this book will provide the factual information for evaluating alternative courses of actions, risks, and methods of measuring results against planned objectives.

Often, a business expects growth in sales and profits from innovations or technological advantages. The risk of potential business interruption may be covered by insurance. A formal business plan projecting detailed growth, sales, costs, and profits by time period may be the basis for settlement in the event of an interruption due to fire, or other policy coverages. This formal plan may prevent lengthy and expensive court cases. It should be developed, or at least recompiled, based on the insurance policy definitions. A sealed, confidential copy should be made available in advance to the insurer for utilization in the event of an interruption.

Business planning should be separated between short-run (one year or less) objectives and long-run (three, five, or more years ahead) strategy. Executive managers must develop basic strategy to include growth, personal selling, product lines, advertising, research, and development goals. Detailed objectives for specific products, cost reductions, media plans, and related items should be handled by middle management. Sometimes plans include an excess of financial statements and projections. These are important guides, but results will be obtained by developing specific strategies with attainable objectives by responsible managers.

Checklist for Business Planning

To develop the total business plan, a scheme should be developed for each specific area of executive responsibility. These could include:

Executive Management
Marketing & Selling
Advertising & Sales Promotion
Research & Development
Manufacturing & Operations
Distribution & Warehousing
Administration
International Operations

I. EXECUTIVE MANAGEMENT

1. What are the annual sales, operating profit, and return on investment objectives for 1970, 1971, and 1974?
2. What is the existing organizational chart, and what new executive positions must be created?
3. What salary, incentive, or training plans are needed to develop or attract the executive talent required?
4. What changes in policies, business activities, or organization may be required to meet the changing sociological needs of people to attract young recruits with executive potential?
5. What are the industry trends, competitors, and competitive conditions expected in the years ahead?
6. What potential new or related business opportunities exist by priority?
7. What are potential acquisitions for new or related businesses, and guideline characteristics or standards which companies must meet to be acceptable acquisition candidates—field of endeavor, profitability, size, trends, etc.?
8. What are the strengths and weaknesses of the firm by major division—sales, R & D, and others?

II. MARKETING & SELLING

1. What are the sales plans by major product group, geographical area, and industry end-use as related to present industry and market position by geographical area?
2. What are the personnel and training requirements for each year?
3. What channels of distribution should be developed—direct retail, distributors, private label, etc.—to maintain control of distribution?
4. What will be the pricing strategy related to competitors—price breaks for volume, quality levels, and brands?
5. What management information systems are required to include sales forecasting, market research, salesman's reports, and statistics?
6. What are the customer service objectives and goals, such as 80 percent of items shipped within 48 hours of receipt of order?
7. What market studies must be initiated to insure that our marketing activities get results and find new market opportunities?

III. ADVERTISING & SALES PROMOTION

1. What are the expected advertising media and point of sale programs?
2. What are the organization and personnel requirements?
3. What will be the advertising agency and relationships?
4. What will be the advertising budgets required to achieve expected growth?
5. Are there additional areas or ways in which advertising could help in achieving goals —such as, maintaining communications with each person in the field, newsletters to customers?

IV. RESEARCH & DEVELOPMENT

1. What plans and programs are required for new product development?
2. What plans will be required to systematically add new products and eliminate old products?
3. What are the organization and personnel requirements for R & D?
4. What are the potential future trends in technology or patents?
5. Are there technical services and literature which should be made available to salesmen and customers?
6. What marketing and technological studies should be initiated to uncover new market opportunities?

V. MANUFACTURING AND OPERATIONS

1. What future plant capacity and locations are required to service expected growth and customers?
2. What personnel and training requirements, including supervisory training programs, are anticipated?
3. What are the trends in labor rates, holidays, and other benefits?
4. What are the industrial relations opportunities and expected union trends?

5. Are plans required for non-financial programs to minimize employee turnover and encourage loyalty, productivity, and satisfaction?
6. Are there improvements in personnel safety and working conditions which are required?
7. What trends are to be expected in automated plant or equipment?
8. What computerized production and inventory control systems are needed?
9. What are the quality and process control targets and goals?

VI. DISTRIBUTION AND WAREHOUSING

1. What are the future trends in the physical movement of goods?
2. What warehouses, capacities, and locations are required to service customer needs?
3. What are the expected freight costs and changes in freight rates?

VII. ADMINISTRATION

1. What are the expected organization, personnel, and training requirements?
2. What are the potential changes or improvements in management information or accounting systems?
3. What data processing requirements and capabilities are needed?
4. What are the anticipated trends and future developments in taxation, and what might their effect be on business goals?
5. Are there expected changes in the requirements for legal resources?
6. What are the projected sales, costs, operating profit, and return on investment projection for the specific years?
7. What are the future working capital needs relative to spending plans?
8. What are the expected capital expenditures, cash flow, cash or loan requirements?
9. What budgets, cost controls, and management reports are required to follow up on plans and objectives?

VIII. INTERNATIONAL OPERATIONS

1. What is the place for international marketing in the business growth—goals and objectives?
2. What are the potential international operations by country or trade group?
3. If international operations are initiated, what type of affiliation, ownership, or requirements should be developed?
4. How should the international marketing be handled within the organization?

Marketing Concept

A successful business plan must be geared to developing a marketing orientation. What is a marketing orientation or marketing concept?

Marketing is not only a department with specific assigned people and functions; it is a philosophy, a way of life. It is the attitude of the customer-oriented firm.

The specific objectives of a marketing-oriented firm are:

1. *Seeking out* and recognizing present or potential demand or customer needs.
2. *Creating* demand through new products, designs, and colors.

3. *Stimulating* demand by means of personal selling, advertising, sales promotion, and pricing.
4. *Servicing* customer needs through effective and efficient distribution.
5. *Keeping* a customer by delivering a quality product backed by a valid guarantee.

Reviewing Corporate Objectives

In order to guide the planning process, managers must formulate the long-range goals or strategies for the business. These should be placed in the form of a General Policy Statement similar to Figure 2-1. These policy objectives should include growth rates, return on investment, sales and marketing goals, and other factors required for planning.

Normal operation is that level of operation which can be expected over the long run for the firm and industry. In high levels of economic activity, a higher level may be achieved; and similarly, in other years below-normal operations may result.

In this policy statement, normal operations are two shifts, five days per week. Though two eight-hour shifts for five days, or 80 hours per week, are expected, this must be related to plant shutdowns, vacations, and holidays. The 80 hours per week, then, may be normal for 48 of 52 weeks or 3,840 hours per year.

Other industries may operate on a one-shift basis. The most likely normal operation is three shifts, five days per week. In continuous process industries, it may be 24 hours per day, seven days per week.

Though advertising, research, and other expenses may have peak years for special programs or events, the standard cost budgets should indicate long-run expectations. This permits variable budgeting of actual year-to-year expenses for control purposes and profit forecasting. Management must define these and other elements of policy to insure reasonable and consistent standard costs.

In this model system, it is assumed the plant will manufacture several types of floor covering. These have been selected to illustrate the difference in costs and pricing for more complex and expensive production machines as contrasted to simpler process conditions.

Other typical problems will cover the change in costs for single versus multiple shift operation and full production versus intermittent production of low volume items. The development of prices for exclusive new products as well as those products which may be in a declining market will be included. In all cases, a control system is designed to achieve specific management objectives, targets, or goals.

In this chapter, the detailed information and planning data will be assembled. In later chapters, these data will be assimilated into a cost calculation and management control system.

Defining the Business Activities

For this book, the illustrated model is a consumer durable goods manufacturer, a tufted carpet firm. The methods and techniques are sufficiently general to be used for assembly operations, continuous processes, and other industries. This example has been

POLICY AND JOB INSTRUCTIONS	Title: COST CONTROL & PROFIT PLANNING

GENERAL POLICY STATEMENT

A profit plan shall be prepared to achieve management's objective return on investment, maximize long-term profits, and seek sound and continuous growth.

The company expects to be marketing oriented - first in new products, designs, customer service, and quality.

Sales shall be aimed at simplified designs for the mass market. Unusual or low volume items are not encouraged.

A system of standard costs and budgets shall be employed. In order to achieve consistent year-to-year cost, the normal or standard volume shall be based on operating three of four tufting machines on a two shift basis.

Sales to mail order or other large volume buyers shall be emphasized, but limited to a maximum of twenty-five percent of total expected sales.

Profit mark-up shall reflect a target of twenty-five percent réturn on gross investment. New, exclusive products with high R & D expense shall be costed to recover all initial expense in five years, on an accelerated declining basis. Profit mark-ups for these items may be over twenty-five percent ROI, as directed by management.

Long run advertising shall be approximately two percent of net sales.

Research and development expense shall be budgeted, in the long run, at two percent of net sales. This may vary from year-to-year as approved R & D projects may require.

Issued By:	Approved By:	Superceded Date: None	Effective Date: xx-xx-xx	No.351.1

FIGURE 2-1
PORTIONS OF A TYPICAL POLICY STATEMENT

chosen because the various analyses involve machine hours, batch processing, chemical formulations, and other components found in typical industries.

A specific, continuous example is being utilized rather than skipping about from one industry situation to another. This will permit the reader to follow the development of a management information system from data collection to control reports.

Once the typical organization is structured, the remaining examples and problems will follow. This will permit the manager, the cost supervisor, the controller, and others to follow the development and implementation of a control system from basic data acquisition through implementation and control.

A similar approach is readily adaptable to any firm, using the related characteristics, specific data, cost centers, and form headings.

The Manufacturing Process

A tufted carpet machine is similar to a sewing machine. Where a sewing machine has, most frequently, one needle, a tufting machine has several hundred needles across its width. Yarn is fed through the needles and sewn into a backing material or cloth which is either jute or a synthetic of some type. Rolls of carpet may be up to 550 linear feet or more in length depending on weight and roll diameter.

Many types of carpet are dyed in dye becks or continuous processes to a particular color—beige, green, etc.—and then dried in a long drying oven. Following this operation, an adhesive is applied to the back of the carpet to cement the yarn to the backing material. Simultaneously, a second backing of jute, foam rubber, or some other material is applied to form a sandwich construction. The process may be visualized easily by observing the cross section of the carpet in a typical office, home, or other installation.

The carpet rolls are inspected and cut into smaller rolls—100', 150', or more—for packaging and shipment to the warehouse or customer. In actual operations, many other roll lengths and types of carpet may be manufactured. The principles applied in this simulated plant may be utilized for these additional processes, product types, and firms.

Organization and Responsibilities

An organizational chart is required listing specific areas of responsibility. This responsibility definition is important in the total control system for the preparation of budgets, and later, variances by responsibility. One type of organization chart is shown in Figure 2-2. This organization chart should be the one planned to achieve the firm's objectives. It need not conform to the existing business organization. A revised organization may be required to achieve the firm's objectives and utilize the available personnel adequately.

In this simulated firm, marketing is responsible for forecasting, market research, and product planning to make products available to manufacturing. Manufacturing is responsible for producing and making first quality products available to Distribution Services. Then, Distribution Services is responsible for order processing, production control, and delivery to a satisfied customer.

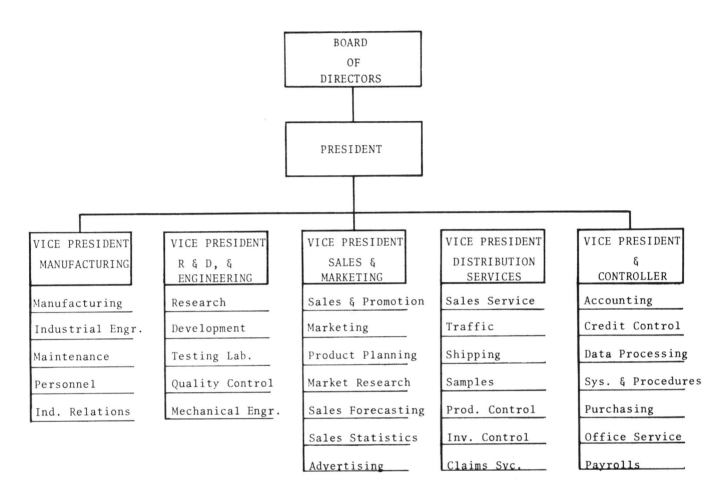

FIGURE 2-2
ORGANIZATION CHART

Typical Products, Parts, or Items

A list of typical manufacturing and sales products, similar to that shown in Figure 2-3 for a carpet firm, is required. This list need not be complete or identical to the product mix. The products should include some items which require processing in all the process or cost centers. It does need to be representative of the items which will account for 60 to 80 percent of the real sales, including unusual, low volume, or other non-standard items. When a complete list of products is not used, the sample selected must be representative of the total product mix. Most likely, deleting products or items with small volume will not distort subsequent cost calculations.

The listing of normal or expected production items is necessary for the development of normal volumes, budget allocations, and expense mark-ups. It is essential for

Product Number	Specification Number	Product Type	Material Description	Stitches Per Inch	Pounds Material Per Unit	First Back	Second Back
101		Level Loop	Filament Nylon	6.0	1.00	Jute	Foam
201		Level Loop	Filament Nylon	7.0	1.28	Jute	Jute
301		Level Loop	Filament Nylon	8.0	2.00	Jute	Jute
401		Pattern	Spun Nylon	6.0	1.00	Jute	Foam
501		Pattern	Spun Acrylic	7.0	1.50	Jute	Jute
601		Pattern	Spun Polyester	8.0	2.00	Jute	Jute

FIGURE 2-3
BASIC DATA FOR NORMAL VOLUME PRODUCTS

management to be able to determine the effect of product mix and color mix variations on subsequent financial results.

Plant Layout and Floor Space Utilization

In order to calculate cost by process, department, or in accounting terms, a cost center, and to differentiate cost for those items which may bypass certain cost centers, a layout, such as Figure 2-4, is helpful. Floor space by cost center is utilized to distribute certain cost elements to cost centers.

Standard Purchased Material Prices

Material losses result from two factors—usage and prices. In order to separate the responsibility for these variances, standard prices, as shown in Figure 2-5, are required.

Usage gains or losses are generally a manufacturing responsibility while variation of actual prices from standard prices is a purchasing function. In some cases, purchasing can miss the standard price when commodity market prices change or, for other reasons, prices are not controlled by the buyer. This is particularly true where fixed price contracts are not utilized. In this case, purchasing is responsible for the analysis and explanation of the variance.

It is also a responsibility of the purchasing function to obtain all price discounts. Often, this requires a special analysis to separate price variances into two components— price and discount gains or losses.

In some situations, gross prices have been used for costing; then, all terms received are credited into one account for distribution over the total range of sales. *This is not correct and it distorts real cost relationships between products or items.* Cost must be based on net prices for materials. Standard terms received must be based on normal

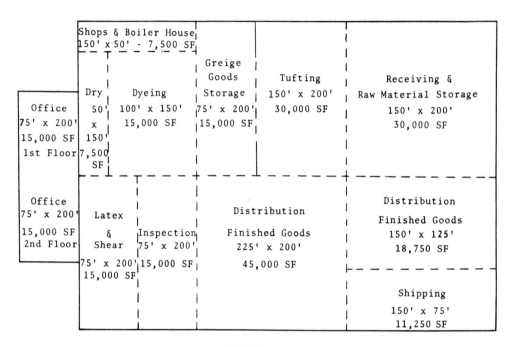

FIGURE 2-4
FLOOR SPACE ALLOCATIONS BY DEPARTMENT

volume usage by raw material item. This is particularly important where variable or direct costing techniques are utilized.

As an example, assume raw material "A" is priced at $1.00, net 30 days and "B" is $1.00, 2% 30 days, and the materials are used in equal amounts. Then Product 1 requires two units of material "A", and Product 2 uses two units of "B".

	Product 1	Product 2
Net cost per unit	$2.00	$1.96
Net cost with average terms	$1.98	$1.98

Using average terms, Products 1 and 2 appear to have an equal raw material cost of $1.98. In fact, this method undercost Product 1 and overcost Product 2 by $0.02 each per unit or a difference between the two products of $0.04 per unit. This difference would distort profitability analysis by product and mislead management's decisions, particularly where thousands or millions of units may be involved.

On some occasions, equal raw materials from different sources of supply have different prices. In this case, a standard price must be set for each source of supply. Then, a weighted average of these standards is used for cost calculation and pricing. This may occur when purchasing wishes to reduce risk of loss of supply by distributing purchases over several buyers.

Material Description	Specification Number	Net Price (FOB Plant)	Unit	Terms
Filament Nylon - 3700 Denier	110	1.17	Lb.	Net 30
Spun Nylon - 840 Lin. Yd.=1 Lb.	120	0.95	Lb.	2%/10 Days
Spun Acrylic - 840 Lin. Yd.=1 Lb.	130	1.20	Lb.	2%/10 Days
Spun Polyester - 840 Lin. Yd.=1 Lb.	140	1.00	Lb.	2%/10 Days
Jute, 9 oz./SY, 150" Wide	224	0.20	SY	Net 30
Jute, 7 oz./SY, 150" Wide	225	1.16	SY	Net 30

SY = Square Yard

FIGURE 2-5
MATERIAL STANDARD PRICES

Some firms may manufacture a portion of the required raw materials and purchase the balance required from outside sources. Generally, the outside source will have a higher price. Assuming the materials are equal and can be substituted or interchanged, a standard price must be established for manufactured materials and each outside source. Here, too, a weighted average price should be used for standard cost based on the expected mix. *It is not correct to cost all the higher priced purchased materials into one product line and manufactured materials into another,* even though this may simplify inventory pricing. The product line with the higher priced materials will appear to have a lower contribution and profit, assuming relative prices for the finished products, solely as a result of costing techniques. This poor performance will not truly reflect market conditions. It will lead the firm out of markets, when, in fact, the firm possibly should continue or expand in a market area.

Should a firm manufacture 75 percent of raw material needs at $0.28 per unit and purchase 25 percent at $0.36 per unit, the average standard raw material price would be:

	Proportion		Standard Price		
Manufactured	0.75	✕	$0.28	=	$0.21
Purchased	0.25	✕	$0.36	=	$0.09
					——————
	Average Standard Price			=	$0.30

Variances from this average standard price would reflect a variation in volume from each source plus a regular price variance by source.

List of Machinery and Replacement Values

For depreciation and investment calculations, a list of major items of machinery by cost or process center is required, as illustrated in Figure 2-6. This must include an expected replacement value for installed equipment in the current market for equivalent or similar equipment. It is important that the replacement value be for equipment with the same production or technological capability. Even though newer, more efficient equipment may be available on the market, replacement prices must be for equipment installed or planned to be installed in the plant.

Tufting Department

Description	Number of Machines	Replacement Value Each
Loop Pile Tufting Machine	6	$ 30,000
Pattern Tufting Machine	6	100,000
Fork Truck	1	10,000
Miscellaneous Equipment		70,000

FIGURE 2-6
LIST OF EQUIPMENT BY PROCESS CENTER

In Chapter Five, the calculation of depreciation will be explained. The effect of these values for investment and pricing is explained in Chapter Nine. In these chapters, typical examples of management problems arising from the use of net depreciated value or original costs are explored.

It is essential in an inflationary economy for management to base cost and prices on replacement values. This permits the recovery of costs in today's market at current dollar values. When original or book costs are used in an inflationary economy, full recovery of sunk costs cannot be obtained, in real dollars.

Though replacement values may be used for cost, pricing, and management control, *these values are not acceptable for external financial reporting or tax accounting.* For these purposes, actual cost and acceptable straight line or accelerated methods must be utilized.

Salary Budgets

Salary budgets by job title and department are necessary for cost calculation. These may be prepared, as shown in Figure 2-7, to include travel expenses and expected bonuses.

The advertising salary budget, including bonuses and travel expense, which con-

Job Title	Staff	Salary	Travel Expenses	Expected Bonus	Total
Sales & Marketing					
VP of Sales & Marketing	1	$ 25,000	$ 5,000	$ 15,000	$ 45,000
Executive Secretary	1	5,000	0	0	5,000
Nat. Acct. Mgr.	1	20,000	5,000	5,000	30,000
Executive Secretary	1	5,000	0	0	5,000
District Managers	6	90,000	30,000	30,000	150,000
Executive Secretary	6	30,000	0	0	30,000
Salesmen	20	240,000	100,000 (Inc. Automobiles)	160,000	500,000
Merchandising Mgr.	1	15,000	1,000	0	16,000
Secretary	1	4,000	0	0	4,000
Market Analyst	1	10,000	500	0	10,500
Design Manager	1	15,000	1,000	1,500	17,500
Commercial Artist	1	10,000	500	1,000	11,500
Design Technicians	1	6,000	0	0	6,000
Advertising Manager	1	15,000	1,000	1,500	17,500
Secretary	1	4,000	0	0	4,000
Clerk	1	4,000	0	0	4,000
Total	45	$498,000	$144,000	$214,000	$856,000

FIGURE 2-7

EXAMPLE OF SALARY BUDGET

forms to the organization chart responsibility shown in Figure 2-2, is $25,500 in Figure 2-7.

These totals should be developed from confidential detail worksheets by person to include expected salary increases in the coming year. The detail budgeting and control of these salaries, and similar expenses will be covered in a later chapter. Some firms may use last year's actual salary cost. This may not be correct if new salary positions have been created or existing salaries increased.

Hourly Labor Complement

Even though the Methods and Standards Department will generally prepare specific labor costs by style based on engineered standards for each cost or process center, the planned labor complement for normal volume operations is necessary for determining labor benefits—social security, unemployment compensation, and others.

A typical labor complement is shown in Figure 2-8. This complement should be for normal operations as defined in the General Policy Statement. For the simulated plant, normal operations are two shifts and five days per week.

Job Title	Shift Complement 1st	2nd	Rate Per Hour	Each $/Week	Total $/Week
	Piece Dyeing				
Dyer & Foreman	1	1	$4.00	$160	$ 320
Dye Weigher	1	1	3.25	130	260
Dye Beck Operator	2	2	3.25	130	520
Loaders/Truckers	6	6	2.25	90	1,080
Clerk/Scheduler	1	1	2.75	110	220
Total	11	11			$2,400

FIGURE 2-8
TYPICAL HOURLY LABOR COMPLEMENT

Where shift differentials are paid for night operations, the rate per hour for the related shift must reflect this shift premium. In the example (Figure 2-8) a shift premium is paid only for third shift operations. This will be illustrated in profit analysis examples (Chapter Ten) of increasing operations from two to three shifts. Standard labor rates should reflect known wage increases in employee contracts or industry wage changes.

Specification Sheets

The foundation for a process and management control system is the complete and detailed specification sheet. It must be based on research and development process capability studies. Specification control limits should be reasonable and achievable in normal production. In most cases, more detailed specifications, supplemented by engineering drawings, will be required than those shown in the carpet example in Figure 2-9.

A process flow chart or listing of the manufacturing processes in sequence is an essential element of the specification sheet. Sometimes, the cost accountant is not familiar with all the processes. On occasions, the cost department may be physically located away from manufacturing operations which causes a loss of "on-the-scene" communications.

As an example, the manufacturing process for the product in the Figure 2-9 specification sheet is:

Number	*Process*
1	Tufting
2	Dyeing
3	Drying
4	Latexing
5	Inspection & Packing

Another product may bypass a process and have a flow of manufacturing processes to include:

Number	*Process*
1	Tufting
4	Latexing
5	Inspection & Packing

Therefore, the processes must be indicated to insure that all costs are included in a cost calculation. This insures, too, that all allowed standard costs will be included in the plant's standard cost for cost control statements.

For cost calculation, specifications must be for the finished, packed product. Each prior manufacturing process may require a different output specification.

Now, the basic data required to begin developing the system has been developed. Administrative and other budgets will be developed at a later point in time.

Cost Calculation Methods

Though a number of terms are used to describe different techniques of cost calculation, the basic methods are *absorption* or total costing, and variable or *direct* costing.

Absorption or total cost involves the distribution or allocation of some fixed ex-

	Product Name: All American	**Product No:** 201

<table>
<tr><td rowspan="6">Carpet</td><td>Carpet Type: Loop</td><td colspan="2">Weight Calculation</td></tr>
<tr><td>Stitches/Inch: 7.0</td><td>Yarn: Spec. 110</td><td>20.5 ± 0.50</td></tr>
<tr><td>Gauge: 5/32"</td><td>1st Back: "   224</td><td>9.0 ± 0.25</td></tr>
<tr><td>Pile Height: 12/32"</td><td>Adhesive   "   324</td><td>26.0 ± 1.00</td></tr>
<tr><td></td><td>2nd Back: "   225</td><td>7.0 ± 0.25</td></tr>
<tr><td>Pile Height: Not Applicable</td><td>Total: (Oz./SY)</td><td>62.5</td></tr>
</table>

Yarn & Backing

Yarn Count: 3700 Denier	1st Back: Jute
Blend: Filament Nylon	Ounces/Square Yard: 9.0
Texture: Level Loop	Width: 150"
Twist - Singles: "Zero" Twist	2nd Back: Jute
Twist - Ply: Not Applicable	Ounces/Square Yard: 7.0
Twist - Cable: " "	Width: 150"

Dyeing & Adhesive

Type Dyeing: Piece Dyeing	Type Adhesive: Synthetic Latex
Method: Open Width	Ounces/Square Yard: 26.0
Process Instructions:	Process Instructions:
Manufacturing Process Procedure No. 92	Manufacturing Process Procedure No. 214

Process & Special Instructions

Tufting: 1	Special Instructions:
Dyeing: 2	
Drying: 3	Tuft: 400 Linear Feet/Roll
Adhesive: 4	Pack: 100 Linear Feet/Roll Specification # 201
Shearing:	133 Square Yards/Roll
Inspection & Packing: 5	

Approvals

Research & Dev.: Date:	
Manufacturing: Date:	
Sales & Marketing: Date:	

Issued by:	Superseded Date: xx-xx-xx	Effective Date: xx-xx-xx	Specification No 501

FIGURE 2-9
EXAMPLE OF SPECIFICATION SHEET

penses; such as, plant management salaries to the process or cost centers. It includes the calculation of all costs elements including material, labor, and fixed expenses in detail.

Variable costing is the separation of each expense into a fixed or variable category. Variable costs have been referred to as direct costs since they occur directly with production or vary with sales volume. With variable costing methods, fixed expenses may be applied in total. Many businesses apply fixed costs by division or product line, even when variable or direct costing is the primary method utilized.

For practical purposes, variable costs—electricity, labor, supplies—are those items which vary as manufacturing volume changes significantly. As production is increased, a larger amount of labor and materials is required.

Absorption costing has been questioned due to the possibility of incorrect allocation and distribution of such elements as corporate office expense to divisions, product lines, and other separations. These lead to incorrect analysis when the product mix or normal volume shifts significantly from the mix or volume which is the basis for expense calculations. Profit forecasting examples in Chapter Ten will illustrate these pitfalls of absorption costing. Yet, upon detailed analysis by expense account, distributions can be based on the "cause" of costs—transactions, people, or square feet.

The application of engineered budget techniques for calculating cost has eliminated the need for distributing many expense accounts. These can now be calculated directly for each cost center.

In the following chapters, cost calculations will be developed which utilize the best of both cost methods for information analysis, cost calculations, and control. The characteristics of a good cost system are:

(a) Understood and supported by management.
(b) Oriented toward management objectives and business control.
(c) Minimize excessive detail or decimal points.
(d) Concentrated on items which significantly affect financial results.
(e) Flexible and easy to change.
(f) Based on acceptable cost accounting practice.

Regardless of the technique involved, managers must understand the "cause and effect" relationship of their decisions on cost calculation, control, and pricing. Effective managers must understand the logic of the control system in order to ask the "right" questions of their staff.

Systematic Planning

In order to insure systematic planning of events, a time series chart of activities is helpful. Figure 2-10 is an example of a new product introduction. A similar chart may be developed for implementing a business cost calculation and control system. Such techniques as CPA (Critical Path Analysis), CPM (Critical Path Method), and PERT (Program Evaluation and Review Technique) are useful. These methods involve a detailed analysis of each project, breaking it down into separate activities, putting each activity into time sequence, and assigning responsibilities, and estimating times.

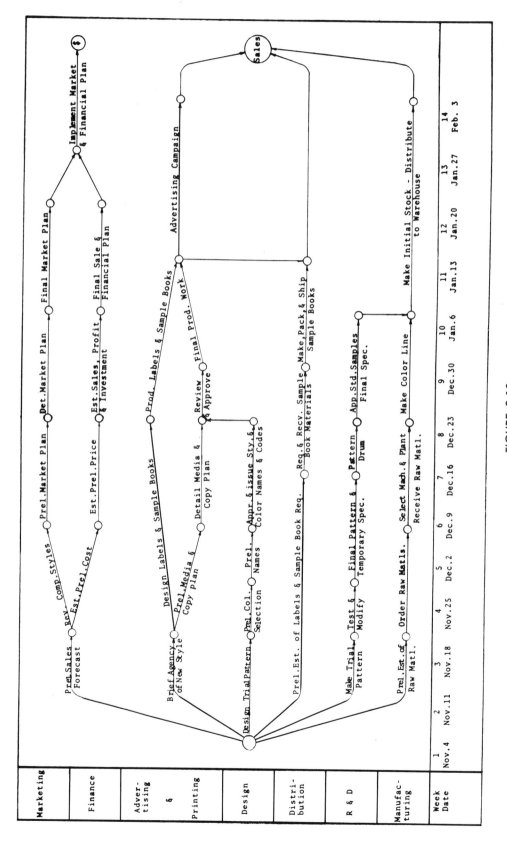

FIGURE 2-10

TIME SERIES CHART OF ACTIVITIES

These methods are good systematic planning tools and provide a method of improving internal communications. In addition, they enable each individual to see his place in the big picture. These charts permit management to follow progress and maintain schedules.

Frequently, an overall chart must be sub-divided into smaller charts for detailed items, as shown in Figure 2-11. These charts may be posted on department or individual bulletin boards to serve as a visual progress chart.

SUMMARY

Planning offers managers opportunities and challenges to organize the future and improve performance. Managers are expected to take the right risk. Yet, risk can be reduced through a factual approach to business judgment.

Though a plan must include financial projections and analyses, effective results will be achieved by executive strategies for the long term and specific objectives or programs and by middle management responsibility for the short term.

The beginning point for a business plan or control system is establishment of the firm's objectives, marketing concept, organization, products, volumes, budgets, and other basic data.

Replacement values are best for plant, property, and equipment as a basis for costing and pricing. These are necessary to recover funds in the current inflated market for replacement of facilities. Replacement values are not acceptable for external financial reporting or tax accounting.

Detail specifications of products and process flow charts are essential to insure an accurate and timely system of calculating cost.

Though a number of terms are used to describe different techniques of cost calculation, the basic methods are *absorption* or total costing, and variable or *direct* costing. In this book, the best features of both techniques are used to analyze information, cost calculation, and control.

Systematic planning techniques of CPA, CPM, and PERT are useful for improving internal communications. They permit managers to follow progress. They enable each person to see his place in the total firm.

The elements of data shown in this chapter are typical of those required to begin planning a management control system. In the following chapter, an engineered approach to developing reliable material cost will be emphasized.

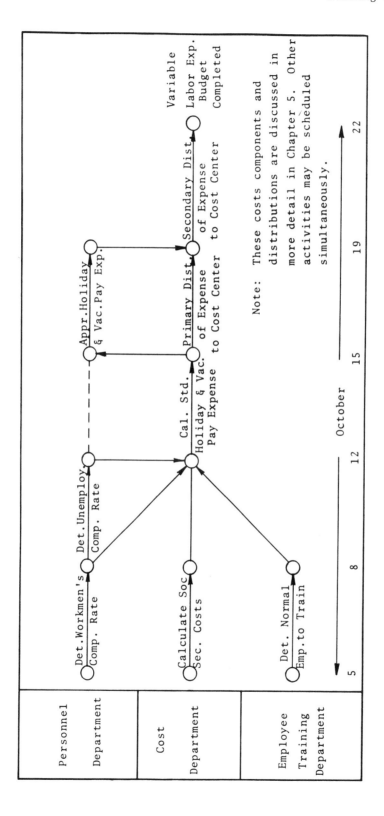

FIGURE 2-11

CHART OF VARIABLE MANUFACTURING LABOR EXPENSE

CHAPTER THREE

Developing Reliable Material Costs

In many industries, the most significant portion of total cost is material costs. The determination of what cost should be and the control of these costs may well be the most important contribution to overall financial results. A unified system of engineered standards, cost control, and inventory valuation is essential.

The needs for material information include:

(a) Initial and inprocess raw materials, parts, or bill of materials, quantities and prices.
(b) Packaging materials specifications and prices.
(c) Material loss or waste generated in the manufacturing process.
(d) Values for inventory prices at the various production processes or cost centers.

Initial Raw Materials

The first step is to determine the basic raw materials for the production process. For the simulated example, these can be transferred from the specification sheet and standard prices developed in Chapter Two. An example of the beginning cost sheet or cost card and raw material data is shown in Figure 3-1, line numbers 1 and 3. The process and materials utilized are:

Process	Materials Utilized
Tufting	Yarn and Backing
Dyeing	Dyestuffs
Latexing	Adhesive and Backing
Inspection & Packing	Packaging Materials

Across the top of the cost sheet are certain elements of information, specifications, and descriptions of the product. One element of information is the "ITEM". In many consumer products, in addition to specification and part numbers, the product is given a "name" for description, advertising, or quality level. An example is the automobile

55

industry with its multiplicity of names to distinguish car types, different advertising appeal, and customer association.

PRODUCT COST SHEET

PLANT ATLANTA	DIVISION HOME FURNISHINGS	SPEC. NO. 501	PRODUCT NO. 201	PRODUCT NAME ALL AMERICAN	CAL. NO. 6102
CAL. BY + DATE	CHECKED BY	MATERIAL WT. 1,280 LB.	MACHINE 5/32 LOOP	SPI SPEC. INSTR. 7.0 NONE	

I T E M	L I N E	ITEM	UNIT	SPEC. NO.	STD. UNITS	MAT. MULT.	ALWD. UNITS	STD. PRICE	COST PER UNIT (SQ. YD.) VARIABLE FIXED TOTAL		
	1	YARN	LB	110	1.280			1.170		X.XXX	
	2	OUTSIDE PROCESS	XX	XXX	X.XXX			X.XXX		X.XXX	
M	3	FIRST BACK	SY	224	1.000			0.200		X.XXX	
A	4	DYE + CHEMICALS								X.XXX	
T E R	5	ADHESIVE								X.XXX	
I A	6	SECOND BACK								X.XXX	
L S	7	PACKAGE								X.XXX	
	8	SUB-TOTAL: MATERIAL COST								X.XXX	

FIGURE 3-1

INITIAL RAW MATERIALS COST AND STANDARD PRICES

Where computers are utilized for cost calculation, the output cost sheet should leave the spaces for "Calculated By" and "Checked By" blank. The person entering the basic data to the program should write in his name indicating a visual checking of the computer cost sheet. Similarly, the person responsible for checking should indicate verification of the computer results.

Other items of information are:

(a) Item—Unit = A listing of materials or parts. This must include the unit. In this case, yarn is in pounds while the first backing is square yards (SY). Where paint is a material, it would be gallons.

(b) Specification Number and Description = The precise specification number used in the product and by the purchasing department.

(c) Standard = Standard amount consumed per "packed" unit of finished product. In the case of materials which are transformed, changed, or converted in the manufacturing process, the standard may be a decimal number; such as 20.5 ounces or 1.280 pounds. For items involving assembly of parts, it would be a whole number 1, 2, etc.

(d) Standard Price = Standard price from the purchasing department.

In some cases, purchased materials may be sent, first, to a subcontractor or processor outside the firm, or to another division of the firm. Should this occur, this outside processing cost should be a separate item on the cost sheet for control purposes. In complex cases, complete cost control reports must be maintained for outside processing materials, costs, and inventory.

Figure 3-1, then, gives the basic raw material data for the initial process. The next step is to develop the inprocess material costs. In the case of the simulated example, the next material to be calculated is dyestuff. For other industries, it may be paint, glue, or fabricated parts—either purchased or fabricated in another department or division of the firm.

A typical dyestuff specification and costs calculation is shown in Figure 3-2, for a unique color "Green". Similar specifications and cost calculations may be developed for any other industry. In some industries, it is necessary to combine specifications and cost calculations to insure that product engineers establish a specification based on both function and cost considerations for an item.

For many consumer items including automobiles, washing machines, and others, it is necessary to manufacture and control cost by individual color. Yet, the wholesale and retail price must be established without regard to color. A gallon of red paint may be priced at retail the same as a gallon of deep blue, although the color pigment cost will be different. The "Green" dyestuff cost may be $0.025 per pound (Figure 3-2) while a "deep blue" dyestuff may be $0.055. This necessitates the calculation of an average cost based on the expected sales by color.

In cost control statements, it is thus necessary to separate variances from standard cost into two components. One is the manufacturing usage gain (or loss); and the second is variation in actual cost due to the variation in actual color mix from the standard color mix. The manufacturing department is responsible for usage variances while the sales management or forecasting function is accountable for color mix changes.

A typical color mix and average cost calculation is shown in Figure 3-3. For management, color mix is extremely important, especially for large contracts for single colors. As an example, assuming a bid is to be entered on 50,000 square yards of carpet which would be equivalent to 100,000 pounds of dyed material, natural color:

> Standard Dyestuff Costs @ $2.80 per 100 Lb. = $2,800
> Actual Dyestuff Costs   @ $0.80 per 100 Lb. =   800
>
> Costs Gain (Loss)   = $2,000 Gain

Similarly, the color variation for blue would be:

> Standard Dyestuff Costs @ $2.80 per 100 Lb. = $2,800
> Actual Dyestuff Costs   @ $5.40 per 100 Lb. = 5,400
>
> Costs Gain (Loss)   = $2,600 Loss

This situation may exist in many consumer goods products where the product in-

Material Description	Standard Price Per Pound	Pounds Material Per 100 Lbs. Carpet	Standard Cost Per 100 Lbs. Carpet
Carpet: Nylon			
Color : Green			
Chemicals			
Chemical A	$0.20	1.75	$0.35
Chemical B	0.06	3.00	0.18
Chemical C	0.22	0.50	0.11
Dyestuffs			
Yellow	$1.70	0.20	$0.34
Scarlet	3.20	0.10	0.32
Blue	6.00	0.20	1.20
Total Cost/100 Pounds of Carpet Dyed	xxxx	xxxx	$2.50
Cost Per Pound			$0.025

Issued By:	Approved By:	Superceded Date None	Effective Date: xx-xx-xx	Specification No. 980

FIGURE 3-2
DYESTUFF SPECIFICATION AND COST CALCULATION

volves color. Significant gains or losses can result from changes in the proportion or mix of colors in actual sales.

In order to be competitive, management must know the real cost by color as well as the average cost for the expected color mix. Analytical forecasting techniques can be used to improve color mix estimates as contrasted with historical averages. When colors change from year to year, the cost of next year's product line must be estimated. The addition or deletion of one or two colors can significantly affect average cost calculations.

Color	Per Cent of Sales (Col. 1)	Cost Per 100 Pounds (Col. 2)	Average Cost (Col. 1 x Col. 2)
Brown	5.0	2.40	$0.12
Sand	10.0	2.00	0.20
Tan	10.0	2.20	0.22
Blue	5.0	5.40	0.27
Rust	10.0	4.70	0.47
Natural	5.0	0.80	0.04
Red	5.0	3.60	0.18
Green	20.0	2.50	0.50
Gold	20.0	2.50	0.50
Beige	10.0	3.00	0.30

Total Average Cost/100
Pounds of Carpet $2.80

Average Cost Per Pound $0.028

FIGURE 3-3
AVERAGE COLOR COST CALCULATION

An example of an Adhesive Specification & Costs Calculation is shown in Figure 3-4. It is necessary for all formula cost to be detailed by item for sound cost calculation and control. In some cases, such as that of the adhesive example, materials must be purchased in liquid form and are dried in the manufacturing process. In such cases, the cost accountant must be careful to consider in his specifications and cost calculations this moisture, liquid, or yield loss. The manager must follow up to insure that the Quality Control Department makes adequate tests on raw materials dry content. The Purchasing Department must verify that price quotations are for identical dry materials content.

A purchased chemical may be $0.20 per gallon less in price from one supplier to another. Yet, to accomplish the purpose or function of the chemical, consumption may be increased by the use of the cheaper chemical. The true or real costs should be based on the "after application" or "after assembly" cost of the purchased product, not the supplier price quotation per unit.

Sometimes, material yield controls are related to standard pounds versus actual pounds consumed. In the case of compounded products, manufacturing can be within a

Material Code	Description	Wet Weight	Dry Weight	Unit	Std. Price	Total Cost
	Adhesive for Jute Back Carpet					
6121	Base Adhesive	420	180	Lb.	$0.30	$54.00
6211	Filler	600	600	Lb.	0.01	6.00
6434	Chemical A	10	1	Lb.	1.20	1.20
6315	Thickner	20	1	Lb.	1.00	1.00
	Total/Batch	1,050	782	-	-	$62.20

Cost/Pound $62.20
Dry   782

= $0.080/Lb.

Issued By:	Approved By:	Superceded Date None	Effective Date: xx-xx-xx	Specification No. 324

FIGURE 3-4
ADHESIVE SPECIFICATION AND COST CALCULATION

reasonable *percent* on pounds; but, significantly *off-target* on dollars. As an example, a 1,000 pound loss of an ingredient which cost $0.30 per pound would be ($300). The same loss of an ingredient which cost $0.01 per pound would be ($10).

Material control reports must be on both pounds or units and dollars for effective and prompt cost analysis and control.

Packaging material specifications and cost calculation should be detailed by item. A chemical industry example is shown in Figure 3-5. Packaging material specifications are required to separate cost by container or package size and special product requirements. Certain chemicals may require stainless steel or more expensive drums. Often, a reuse factor and recondition cost must be included when containers can be reused. In the example in Figure 3-5, the question for management may be "Yes, a plastic container is specified; but, is there available another type plastic which will perform the same function at less cost?"

Material Code	Description	Unit	Quantity	Std. Price	Total Cost	Tare Weight
	Specification 2-14 Case, 4-one gallons					
1022	Jugs, plastic, gallon	Each	4	$0.20	$0.80	
4131	Carton, 8-1, gallon	Each	1	0.40	0.40	
7091	Caps, #40, black	Each	4	0.02	0.08	
	Total Cost/Case				$1.28	5.50
	Total Cost/Gallon				$0.32	
	Specification 8-71 Drum, 55 gallon					
3134	Drum, steel, 55 gallon	Each	1	$7.50	$7.50	
9099	Faucet & Clip	Each	1	0.20	0.20	
	Total Cost/Drum				$7.70	38.00
	Total Cost/Gallon				$0.14	

Issued By:	Approved By:	Superceded Date None	Effective Date: xx-xx-xx	Specification No. 9210

FIGURE 3-5
PACKAGING MATERIAL SPECIFICATION AND COST CALCULATION

A small change in cost for items used in large volumes will result in a significant change in profits. These gains may be individually small, but they are collectively significant since they are all profit.

Now material specifications and costs have been completed. The original Figure 3-1 example can be expanded to include inprocess and packaging materials as indicated in Figure 3-6, line numbers 4, 5, 6, and 7.

PRODUCT COST SHEET

PLANT ATLANTA		DIVISION HOME FURNISHINGS		SPEC. NO. 501		PRODUCT NO. 201		PRODUCT NAME ALL AMERICAN		CAL. NO. 6102

CAL. BY ◆ DATE   CHECKED BY   MATERIAL WT. 1,280 LB.   MACHINE 5/32 LOOP   SPI 7.0   SPEC. INSTR. NONE

ITEM	LINE	ITEM	UNIT	SPEC. NO.	STD. UNITS	MAT. MULI.	ALWD. UNITS	STD. PRICE	COST PER UNIT (SQ. YD.) VARIABLE	FIXED	TOTAL
	1	YARN	LB	110	1.280			1.170		X.XXX	
	2	OUTSIDE PROCESS	XX	XXX	X.XXX			X.XXX		X.XXX	
M A T E R I A L S	3	FIRST BACK	SY	224	1.000			0.200		X.XXX	
	4	DYE ◆ CHEMICALS	LB	980	1.850			0.028		X.XXX	
	5	ADHESIVE	LB	214	1.625			0.080		X.XXX	
	6	SECOND BACK	SY	225	1.000			0.160		X.XXX	
	7	PACKAGE	SY	9210	1.000			0.030		X.XXX	
	8	SUB-TOTAL: MATERIAL COST								X.XXX	

FIGURE 3-6
MATERIALS AND STANDARD PRICES

Material Loss Standards

The term "waste" or "scrap" is frequently used to denote material losses. Both of these have, in the minds of people, a connotation or implication of little or no value. Therefore, these terms should probably be discarded in favor of terminology which properly emphasizes the value of materials which are lost in process and do not reach the finished product.

The first step in material loss control is to develop sound standards. Industrial engineers must apply analytical approaches to developing material loss standards.

Sometimes, percentages of historical averages may be utilized. They only tell management what losses have been in the past. They do not indicate what losses *should be* nor point-up areas for potential cost reduction.

In most cases, material loss standards can be specified and calculated as in Figure 3-7. This involves the development of a Material Loss Specification to include:

(a) Department
(b) Type material
(c) Description
(d) Collection of material
(e) Formula for calculating standard loss
(f) Allowed loss per unit of production
(g) Allowed loss per week in pounds
(h) Cost per pound of material loss

Specifications of this type can be developed for most industries. The key is determining a formula for calculation of the amount of material loss expected which reflects variables in the process.

Losses in both linear units of measure and pounds are required. Though the production reporting unit may be in a linear measurement unit, materials losses are generally collected in containers which require reporting the loss in pounds.

Accurate standards provide the basis for initiation of investigation into the "causes" of material losses, as well as a target or goal for performance. Standards are changed as the production mix changes. They help the cost accountant more accurately estimate costs.

As an example, a material loss standard may be based on one faulty fiber washer per 1,000 units assembled. If specifications change to a type which results in the loss of two washers per 1,000 units assembled, the material loss will increase, regardless of the operating or process control in the manufacturing department. Engineered standards and managerial control methods enable management to revise standards in advance of changes. They insure that management places the responsibility for gains or losses on the responsible department.

Nothing creates more friction or deterioration in working relationships than for a plant manager to state to a department manager, "Bill, your material losses are way out of line this week. What happened to your process control?" Then, upon investigation, the department manager finds that the production mix or specifications have changed to cause higher losses—without a change in control standards.

Sometimes, engineering studies may show that more material should be lost to reach optimum machine and operator performance.

The utilization of historical waste percentages and comparisons with other plants with varying conditions, production mix, and equipment is obsolete in this age of technology and engineering achievement.

In some more complex cases involving multiple operator machine assignments and machine interference, the theories of mathematical probability and statistics provide additional engineering basis for sound material loss standards. These improved material standards enable the engineered calculation of optimum operator cycle time and machine assignments.

For assembly operations, chemical production, food processing industries, and others, an industrial engineer can develop analytical standards for improved cost calculation and control. In pricing, it is the small refinement that enables the cost accountant

Department   : Adhesive

Type Waste   : Selvage Trim Waste

Description   : Trim waste cut off each side of carpet.

Collection of Waste: Waste collected each shift, weighed and
                      recorded on Waste Record Sheet.

$$\text{Calculation of Standard Per Linear Yard of Carpet} = \left[\left(\frac{A}{36} \times \frac{B}{16}\right) + C + D + \left(\frac{E}{36} \times \frac{F}{16}\right)\right] \times 2$$

Example: A = Standard width of primary back trim waste, 3"
          B = Ounces per square yard of primary back
          C = Pounds per linear yard of latex
              determined by Waste Study, = .075
          D = Pounds per linear yard of yarn determined
              by Waste Study - 2 Rows, = .010
          E = Standard width of secondary back trim waste, 3"
          F = Ounces/square yard of secondary back

$$\text{Allowed Pounds Per Lin. Yd. Latexed} = \left[\left(\frac{3}{36} \times \frac{9}{16}\right) + .075 + .010 + \left(\frac{3}{36} \times \frac{7}{16}\right)\right] \times 2$$

$$= (0.047 + .075 + .010 + .036) \times 2$$

$$= 0.168 \times 2 = 0.336 \text{ Pounds/Linear Yard}$$

Allowed Pounds/Week: Linear Yards X 0.336
                      Double Jute Back

Waste Cost:

Primary Back	:	0.168 SY	X	0.200	=	$ 0.0336
Latex	:	0.150 Lb	X	0.080	=	$ 0.0120
Yarn	:	0.020 Lb	X	1.170	=	$ 0.0234
Secondary Back:		0.168 SY	X	0.160	=	$ 0.0269
						$ 0.0959

$$\text{Waste Cost/Pound} = \frac{\$0.0959}{0.336} = \$ 0.286$$

FIGURE 3-7
MATERIAL LOSS SPECIFICATION

to calculate the costs more precisely, and management to quote on contracts with a feeling of security.

As an example, a manufacturer may be quoting on an automotive part for 650,000 units in one contract. The quotation is $6.97 per unit. The contract could be lost to a competitor for $6.86 per unit. Upon the development of calculated engineered standards, the material loss for this specific part was found to be $0.30; whereas an average loss of $0.42 was used in the $6.97 per unit quotation. In this case, a contract may be lost as well as $42,000 in profit, and $105,000 in contribution to fixed costs and profit combined. This loss would be a direct result of the lack of precise material loss standards.

As the customer requires more specialized products, and as more large buyers enter the field, management must know its real costs differentiated by product, by item, by color, and other important features.

Historical calculations and average costing lead to an average performance of the firm. There is not much difference between the top firm and an average one—yet, the difference is all profit!

Material Control

Given, then, that engineered specifications and material loss standards are available, the next step is usage reporting, production reporting, and control. A key element of information is the *net output production* by cost or process center.

The first control report is a report of material analysis or yield; that is, the input of raw materials per unit of production—batch, piece, or linear yard. For the simulated firm, this report might appear as shown in Figure 3-8. Similar reports can be prepared for other industries by substituting the appropriate manufacturing departments and materials. Packaging materials may also be included on a report of this format.

Notice that there are no percentages on this report. The true statistic for management is the magnitude of the gain or (loss) in dollars. Sometimes, management emphasizes large percentage losses when the dollar value is trivial.

The analysis of gain (or loss) is important for management attention.

(a) *Usage*—It is the responsibility of the manufacturing supervisor to insure that equipment is properly adjusted and specifications are followed relative to input of the required material, within quality control limits.

(b) *Price*—It is the responsibility of the Purchasing Department to purchase materials at standard prices.

(c) *Material Loss*—The manufacturing supervisor is responsible for controlling material loss. The specific loss may be taken from the Material Loss Analysis. A portion of such an analysis is shown in Figure 3-9.

(d) *Inventory*—Material consumption may not be accurately reported. Occasionally, a manufacturing supervisor will fail to follow up to insure that materials lost are correctly weighed. Physical inventories will detect the difference in actual versus reported consumption by inventory auditing.

DIVISION: HOME FURNISHINGS   DATE: XX-XX-XX   PLANT: ATLANTA

DEPARTMENT MATERIAL-UNIT	UNITS (00)			DOLLARS (00)			ANALYSIS OF GAIN (LOSS) - $00				
	STD. USAGE COL. 1	ACTUAL USAGE COL. 2	GAIN (LOSS) CCL. 3	STD. USAGE COL. 4	ACTUAL SID. PRICES COL. 5	ACTUAL USAGE ACTUAL PRICES COL. 6	USAGE	PRICE	MATL. LOSS	INVENTORY	TOTAL
TUFTING DEPT											
NYLON -LB											
PCLYESTER -LB											
ACRYLIC -LB											
BACKING -LY											
SUB-TOTAL:											
DYEING + DRYING DEPT.											
CHEMICALS -LB	94,400	93,200	1,200	$9,440	$9,300	$120	($70)	$80	$110	$00	$120
DYES -LB											
SUB-TOTAL:											
LATEXING DEPT.											
BACKING -LY											
ADHESIVE -LB											
CTHER -LB											
SUB-TOTAL:											
PLANT TOTAL	XXXX	XXXX	XXXX								

FIGURE 3-8
MATERIALS ANALYSIS REPORT

DATE: XX-XX-XX
DIVISION: STEEL FABRICATION   PLANT: PITTSBURGH

MATERIAL LCSS CLASS	DEPARTMENT MATERIAL	U N I T S (00)			D O L L A R S		
		STANDARD	ACTUAL	GAIN (LOSS)	STANDARD	ACTUAL	GAIN (LOSS)
	MANUFACTURING						
1	MATERIAL "A"						
	CLASS 1	1,400	1,480	(80)	$700	$740	($40)
	CLASS 2						
	CLASS 3						
2	MATERIAL "B"						
	CLASS 1						
	CLASS 2	120	140	(20)	1,200	1,400	($200)
	CLASS 3						
3	MATERIAL "C"						
	SUB-TOTAL:						

FIGURE 3-9
MATERIAL LOSS ANALYSIS

Calculations of Gains (or Losses)

The usage gain (or loss) may be calculated by comparing actual usage to standard usage or:

$$\frac{\text{Actual Usage}}{\text{at Standard Prices}} - \frac{\text{Standard Usage}}{\text{at Standard Prices}} = \text{Usage Gain (or Loss)}$$

For the example displayed in Figure 3-8, this is column 2 minus column 1. A price variance can be found by subtracting actual usage at standard prices from actual usage at actual prices. This is on Figure 3-8, column 6 minus column 5.

Material gain (or loss) may be taken from scrap reports, Figure 3-9, by class of waste comparing actual to standard performance by department. Inventory variance can be obtained from physical inventory analysis.

Reports of this type may be produced weekly, monthly, or for some other time interval as may be feasible for the particular firm. Another column may be added to give a four week average gain (or loss) total. These reports may be filed for visual analysis, or control charts may be plotted for time series analysis.

In this example, only the important materials have been included. This permits management to concentrate time and attention on those *few* items which significantly affect results.

When a large gain (or loss) is reported, it is necessary to do a more detailed study of these data by style, item, or part. Similarly, a special analysis may be essential to separate the gains (or losses) due to color mix variation from the standard mix. This involves the multiplication of production by the individual color cost, then, multiplying the same production by the average color cost. The difference is the effect of color mix on gains (or losses).

In the example shown in Figure 3-10, a loss of $1,080 results from the color mix of actual production. The production department manager has no control and should not be held responsible for this loss.

In plants where material reporting systems utilize data processing equipment, both the total and subsidiary reports may be obtained on a monthly, weekly, daily, and in some cases, on an individual shift or job lot basis. However, managers must insist on

Color	Production (100 Pounds)	Unit Standard Cost	Total Allowed Standard Cost
Brown	100	$2.40	$ 240
Sand	200	2.00	400
Tan	100	2.20	220
Blue	400	5.40	2,160
Rust	400	4.60	1,840
Natural	200	0.80	160
Red	100	3.60	360
Green	200	2.50	500
Gold	200	2.50	500
Beige	100	3.00	300
Total-Actual Standard Cost	2,000		$6,680
Total-Average Standard Cost	2,000	$2.80	$5,600
Gain or (Loss) due to color mix			($1,080) Loss

FIGURE 3-10
CALCULATION COLOR MIX VARIATION

receiving only those reports which point up potential cost control losses. Then, when a significant loss occurs, detail reports should be easily obtainable on an exception basis.

Management must not permit systems and planning departments, data processing or other departments to burden them with excess paper or reports from which no effective or timely decision can be implemented.

Multipliers for Cost Calculation

Now that standards have been developed and cost control reports have been set up, the cost accountant must use these data to calculate cost and price the inventory in process, as well as finished goods. All costs are calculated on a *finished or packed* unit ready for shipment.

It is necessary for cost accounting to mark up labor and materials for material loss and production which passes through a cost or production center, but does not reach the finished or packed production. As an example, a roll of electric cable may be 3,000 linear feet. Yet, with material losses, quality samples, and other causes, only 2,950 feet may reach packed production. Manufacturing process labor and materials must be marked-up to recover these losses.

An example of calculations are detailed in Figure 3-11. Material losses are in two categories, saleable and reworkable. Saleable is that material which must be sold and is not reusable. Reworkable is that material which can be reused again in the process; and therefore, is not a material loss. Reworkable, then, is included in the labor multiplier factor; but, it is not a factor in material loss multipliers.

Figure 3-11 is a generalized example. Those applicable to the simulated firm are included on the completed material costs calculations, Figure 3-12.

The allowed standard line 1, Figure 3-12, is:

$$\frac{\text{Specification}}{\text{Standard}} \times \frac{\text{Material Loss}}{\text{Multiplier}} = \frac{\text{Allowed}}{\text{Standard}}$$

$$\text{Yarn-Lbs.} = \quad 1.280 \quad \times \quad 1.035 \quad = \quad 1.325$$

The material cost, which is a "variable" cost is:

$$\frac{\text{Allowed}}{\text{Standard}} \times \frac{\text{Standard}}{\text{Price}} = \frac{\text{Cost Per}}{\text{Square Yard}}$$

$$\text{Yarn-Lbs.} - 1.325 \text{ Lbs.} \times \$1.170 = \$1.551$$

In cases where materials stretch or shrink in the manufacturing process, these gains or losses must be included.

These multipliers indicate that a raw material valued at $1.17 per pound purchased price has an inprocess value at process "B" of $1.22 (Figure 3-11, Col. 7, Row 15). And, since only 89 pounds per 100 input pounds reach packed production, Department "A" labor must be marked-up 1.044 (Figure 3-11, Col. 11, Row 8) for subsequent

Worksheet For Material Loss Multipliers

(1) Material Loss Class	(2)	(3) Type Loss	(4) Pounds	(5) Cost or Sale Value Per Pound	(6) Total Col.4 x Col.5	(7) Value Per Output Pound Col.6 ÷ Col.4	(8) Material Loss Multiplier Col.7 ÷ Col.7 Row	(9)	(10) Pounds	(11) Multiplier Col.10 ÷ Row	(12)	(13)
Net Input Department A			100.00	1.17	117.00	1.170	1.062		100.00	1.122		
	Class 1	Saleable	4.00	0.50	2.00				4.00			
	Class 2	Reworkable	—	—	—				3.00			
Net Output			96.00		115.00	1.200	1.058	Example 1.245/1.200	93.00	1.044	Example 93.00/89.00	
Department B												
	Class 4	Saleable	2.00	0.10	0.20				2.00			
Net Output			94.00		114.80	1.220	1.020		91.00	1.022		
Department C												
	Class 5	Saleable	1.00	0.10	0.10				1.00			
Net Output			93.00		114.70	1.234	1.008		90.00	1.010		
Department D												
	Class 6	Saleable	1.00	0.20	0.20				1.00			
Net Output			92.00		114.50	1.245	1.000		89.00	1.000		

Material Multiplier / Labor Multiplier

Prepared By / Approved By — Initials / Date

FIGURE 3-11

WORKSHEET FOR MATERIAL LOSS MULTIPLIERS

PRODUCT COST SHEET

PLANT ATLANTA	DIVISION HOME FURNISHINGS		SPEC. NO. 501		PRODUCT NO. 201		PRODUCT NAME ALL AMERICAN		CAL. NO. 6102
CAL. BY + DATE	CHECKED BY		MATERIAL WT. 1,280 LB.		MACHINE 5/32 LOOP	SPI 7.0	SPEC. INSTR. NONE		

I T E M	L I N E	ITEM	UNIT	SPEC. NO.	STD. UNITS	MAT. MULT.	ALWD. UNITS	STD. PRICE	COST PER UNIT (SG. YD.) VARIABLE	FIXED	TOTAL
	1	YARN	LB	110	1.280	1.035	1.325	1.170	1.551	X.XXX	1.551
	2	OUTSIDE PROCESS	XX	XXX	X.XXX	X.XXX	X.XXX	X.XXX	X.XXX	X.XXX	X.XXX
M A T E R I A L S	3	FIRST BACK	SY	224	1.000	1.020	1.020	0.200	0.204	X.XXX	0.204
	4	DYE + CHEMICALS	LB	980	1.850	1.075	1.990	0.028	0.056	X.XXX	0.056
	5	ADHESIVE	LB	214	1.625	1.050	1.710	0.080	0.137	X.XXX	0.137
	6	SECOND BACK	SY	225	1.000	1.020	1.020	0.160	0.163	X.XXX	0.163
	7	PACKAGE	SY	9210	1.000	1.025	1.025	0.030	0.031	X.XXX	0.031
	8	SUB-TOTAL: MATERIAL COST							2.142	X.XXX	2.142

FIGURE 3-12

COMPLETED MATERIAL COST CALCULATION

losses. Therefore, if Department "A" labor cost is $0.10 per net output unit, the finished unit cost is $0.10 × 1.044 = $0.104.

Multipliers, of this type, may be necessary for each material type. They may be calculated using the unit of measure related to the product—pounds, linear measurement, or individual part.

Cost of Sales

The standard cost which has been developed by item will be the basis for valuation of cost of sales and inventories. Subsequent reports shall illustrate variances from these standard costs which must be entered into the financial record to arrive at an actual cost for financial reporting. The details of these transactions are included in other text on general or cost accounting.

Electronic data processing is required in a complex business to properly account for cost by item. Manual computation may not be economically feasible in some firms.

SUMMARY

Material cost may be the most significant portion of total cost for many industries. Faulty material cost calculations which do not point up cost differences by product can lead to loss of sales and profit potential.

To obtain proper cost, material cost and scrap losses should be calculated based on specifications and engineered scrap losses. Determination of engineered scrap losses is explained. Where color is involved, calculations should be by individual color for cost control and pricing large volume requirements.

Chemical usage must be specified by item. Control should be concentrated on those few items which generate a large portion of the cost dollars. The text includes examples of color, chemical, packaging, and other material specifications, calculations, and control reports.

Historical calculations and average costing lead to an average performance firm. There is not much difference between a top firm and an average one. Yet, it is all profit.

Now, with material standards and costs calculated, the next chapter illustrates the compiling of valid labor costs. In the latter chapters, the standards now being derived and costs being calculated will tie together into a coordinated management control system for all levels of management—first-line supervision, department manager, plant manager, and executive management.

CHAPTER FOUR

Compiling Valid Labor Costs

The determination and control of labor costs is an important function of an industrial cost control system. In industries where labor cost is a large part of total cost, the control of labor and labor related expenses will likely take on added significance since the uncontrolled portion may be the difference between a profit or a loss.

On the national scene, labor costs have been increasing rapidly over recent years. In order to maintain the competitive position, management must constantly analyze labor cost and implement new ways of increasing productivity by eliminating the need for labor through automation, introducing improved product designs, or developing improved methods.

The main elements of manufacturing expenses or costs incurred in manufacturing a product are material, labor, and factory expenses. The determination and control of material cost was covered in Chapter Three. Sometimes, other terms are used for factory expenses. The two major classifications of factory expenses are variable manufacturing expenses and fixed manufacturing expenses. These will be the subject of a subsequent chapter.

Labor costs include payments direct to the employee as well as variable labor expenses including social security, vacation pay, holiday pay, unemployment insurance, workmen's compensation insurance, and employee training. Specific industries or firms may have labor related expenses which are unique to that industry, firm, or union contract. These expenses could include such elements as paid lunch breaks, certain union activities, reporting pay, and shift premium. Hospitalization insurance for manufacturing personnel and other fixed costs will be included under fixed manufacturing expenses.

Variable and Fixed Expense Classifications

Much has been written about the classification of expenses into the variable or fixed categories. For practical purposes, expenses are variable if they change when the plant operations change from, say, three to four, five, or six days per week of operation.

These variable expenses include productive labor, raw materials, electricity, fuel, and others. Depreciation, plant management and supervisor salaries, taxes, and similar items which do not change with the level of operation are considered as fixed costs.

Those using this method of classification usually assume that variable expenses change in a straight line or linear relationship as the level of plant or department operation changes. This may not always be true. Some cost may vary in a non-linear manner. Unless such variation from a linear relationship significantly affects the real cost, this assumption of a straight line variation will be satisfactory for practical application.

Where data are available, a test of the variation of a particular expense item may be made by plotting the actual cost of expenses; such as electricity versus department operations, as shown in Figure 4-1. In this case variation does occur from the straight line. Yet, this variation is insignificant within a reasonable range of hours of operation.

In situations where sufficient data are available, statistical methods may be used to evaluate the significance of the variation more precisely. Graphs, manual calculations,

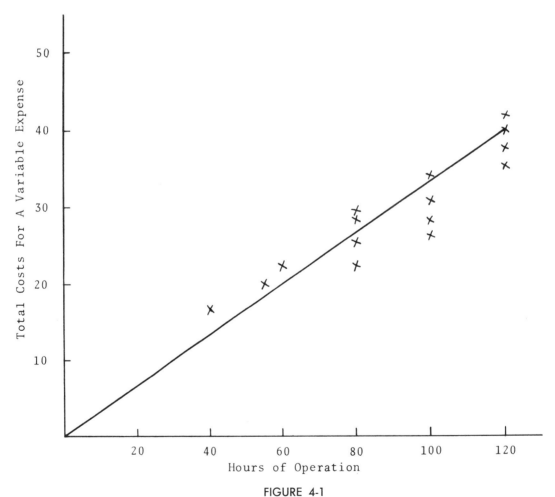

FIGURE 4-1

CHART OF DEPARTMENT OPERATION VERSUS A VARIABLE EXPENSE

or computer systems can be utilized to determine the significance of variation and as an aid in the development of formulas for the prediction of expenses with non-linear variations.

Company policy and management decisions must be considered in determining expenses which are variable. Some particular jobs, either in plant clerical, maintenance, or other areas, may be an hourly rate; however, policy may guarantee a minimum of forty hours per week. In these cases, the costs are fixed.

Guides to how variable or direct costs behave or react are:

(1) When there is no production of goods or services, there are no variable costs.
(2) The relationship of variable cost to production tends to be proportional.
(3) As contrasted to fixed cost, variable cost is not a function of time.

Fixed costs are often referred to as period or sunk costs. Although in many instances fixed costs do not change within a given range of activity, they can change from year to year as executive salaries are changed, property taxes are increased, or insurance premiums are revised. Business planning in excess of one year must provide for these types of changes in fixed cost.

Sometimes personnel policy may not be adhered to rigidly. As an example, some shift foremen may be on a salary basis whereas other shift foremen may be on an hourly rate. For the classification of variable versus fixed expense, the job policy is the controlling criteria, not a particular individual or situation. However, problems of this type will create cost control problems and make plant-to-plant comparisons of costs invalid.

Some cost items are semi-variable for given levels of plant operation or plant capacity utilization. The foremen's salaries may increase when operations expand from two to three shifts. However, given a planning policy of long-run, two-shift operations, this cost is fixed. Therefore, the classification of costs as either variable or fixed should be consistent with management's long-range planning objective and policy statements.

In the garment and poultry industry, one shift operation may be normal. For automotive and other assembly lines, normal operations may be two shifts at a constant efficiency for the assembly line, even though year-to-year operations may vary from one to three shifts or work turns. For industries such as steel, textiles, and others with high investments as related to labor cost, the more likely multiple shifts should be feasible and adopted as a management policy.

Direct, Indirect, or Productive Labor

In some firms, labor cost has been classified as direct or indirect. Direct labor was believed to be that labor or those jobs which could be directly related to production. In a machine parts plant, a lathe operator could be considered direct. Indirect labor was that work which could not be directly associated with production. Indirect jobs included materials handling, lift truck operators, mechanics, and others who worked on multiple work assignments or departments. This led management to concentrate its efforts on controlling direct labor and, on occasions, ignoring indirect labor. As a result, it has *not* been common for indirect labor with loose controls to exceed direct labor.

In some instances, jobs have been classified as direct or indirect based on whether it was feasible to develop an industrial engineering standard or incentive rate for the job. With present techniques, trained work measurement personnel can determine a reasonable standard for labor for most jobs, either clerical, maintenance, or shipping. Therefore, the terms direct and indirect are being discarded in favor of the term productive labor. Alfred Sloan adopted this concept of productive labor in his early years with General Motors in the 1920's.

The expenditure of any business resource, labor, computer reports, or other work, is either productive and should be controlled, or it should be eliminated.

Basis for Labor Costs

The determination of labor standards is normally a responsibility of the Methods and Standards Department. The industrial engineering procedures for work measurement, machine interference, and optimum operator assignments are covered in other references. These include time and motion study, ratio delay techniques, and statistical studies.

Often, we think only of reducing labor costs or eliminating jobs. Sometimes, however, improved cost performance considering labor, materials, and fixed costs, may require increasing jobs or labor costs to eliminate machine interference and other inefficiencies. In evaluating standard labor cost for operator assignments, effective managers must insist that all labor elements, including plant productivity, be considered. Sometimes Methods and Standards Engineers evaluate labor cost only, and ignore material loss, fixed cost, and other productivity related expenses.

Managers may obtain indication of the areas to concentrate attention for cost control and cost reduction by analyzing the proportion of direct cost. For different industries these relationships could be:

	Percent by Company		
	A	B	C
Materials	70	35	30
Labor	10	35	50
Variable Manufacturing Expense	20	30	20
	100	100	100

Company "A" should concentrate first on material cost for cost control and reduction. A balanced firm, Company "B", would require control in all areas, possibly concentrating on the major elements in each area. Company "C" would give primary attention, initially, to labor cost, then move to material cost to improve control. This sequence is an indication of priority. All economically feasible elements of cost must eventually be brought under tight control.

Where a Methods and Standards Department is available, labor cost by product number, by job and/or operation should be summarized and recorded in a manner similar to Figure 4-2. Data of this type can be used directly for costs calculations and control statements.

DYEING DEPARTMENT LABOR STANDARDS

Effective Date:
xx-xx-xx

Issued By:

Approved By:

Product Number	Size	Proc. No.	Key Operating Data				Standard Labor Cost Per 100 Square Yards					
			Mach. Hr. Per Batch	Sq. Yd. Per Batch	Sq. Yd. Per Mach. Hr.	Mach. Hr. Per 100 SY	Total	Dyer	Dye Weigh	Operators	Load Truck	Clerk
201	12'	92	3.2	533	166.6	0.60	$1.491	0.195	0.163	0.326	0.675	0.132
619	12'	114	4.0	500	125.0	0.80	1.984	0.259	0.216	0.434	0.900	0.175
990	12'	216	6.0	500	83.3	1.20	2.979	.390	.325	0.651	1.350	0.263

FIGURE 4-2

METHODS AND STANDARDS LABOR COST SUMMARY

It is essential that labor cost be calculated by individual products rather than by a historical average condition. In the example in Figure 4-2, Product Number 990's cost is almost double that of Product Number 201. Later, in calculating fixed cost, the fixed manufacturing cost will show a similar increase due to the lower productivity per machine hour of Product Number 990. Not only does this higher requirement for equipment by Product Number 990 increase costs, it also cuts down the overall productivity of the plant. Conditions of this type are found in almost all industrial operations.

With actual, detailed cost data by product, linear programming and other mathematical techniques can be used in product mix and resource allocation to maximize productivity and contribution to fixed cost or profits.

In batch processes such as chemicals and certain other assembly operations, labor cost may be so small as to appear insignificant. However, even in these industries, these costs must be separated by job or cost center for cost control purposes. Often, in situations where labor costs are small, there are products among those produced which require an abnormal amount of machine time; and consequently, have a high fixed cost which lowers overall plant productivity.

As an example, liquid chemical "A" may require a mixing time of five minutes per 4,000 gallons; whereas chemical "B" may require a slow mixing and stabilization time of sixty minutes for a given quantity. Even though the chemical "B" labor cost may be the same as chemical "A" for weighing each batch, the additional machine time of chemical "B" will represent a higher variable and fixed cost. In situations involving chemical powder mixing, the blending time may be identical for various powders; yet, the packaging time, loading of weight hoppers, and movement to blenders by auger type conveyors can vary significantly based on the distance and density of the materials involved.

In all cases, the labor and machine hour requirements must be determined either by Methods and Standards engineers or the best management estimates. Cost calculations and cost control by historical averages leads to incorrect management decision information and failure to attain competitive performance.

Some existing control systems may be more oriented toward costing products, inventory calculation, and financial reporting, rather than planning and control. Once goals, budgets, and standards are planned and established, management needs to know when the objectives have not been attained, or more important, when to highlight areas or costs which are getting out-of-line.

Cost Center Worksheet

A first step in labor cost calculation is to set up a Cost Center Worksheet similar to Figure 4-3. In this example, the Dyeing Department labor cost which is covered by the Methods and Standard Summaries is $2,400. This was previously determined in Chapter Two, Figure 2-8, the Hourly Labor Complement.

The next step is to determine the number of standard or normal volume machine hours for each cost center. In this case, the department contains twelve machines operating two shifts or eighty hours per week per machine for a total of 960 ma-

Cost Center Worksheet
Dyeing Department

	Initials	Date
Prepared By		
Approved By		

(1)	(2)	(3)	(4) ← Labor Methods & Standard Summary	(5) Cost → Service Dept.	(6)	(7) Variable Labor Benefits	(8) Cost/Week Mfg. Expense	(9)	(10) Fixed Mfg. Expense	(11)	(12)	(13)
Labor Cost/Week			#2400									
Number of Machines			12									
Operating Hours 2 Shifts, 40 Hours each			X 80									
Total Machine Hours			= 960									
Cost Per Machine Hour			#2.50									

BURROUGHS CORPORATION TODD COMPANY DIV. Form H513

FIGURE 4-3
INCOMPLETE COST CENTER WORKSHEET

chine hours per week. The cost per machine hour, then, is line 2 ($2,400) divided by line 9 (960 machine hours) or $2.50.

The costs for service departments, variable costs, and fixed costs will be determined in later calculations. A similar worksheet would be prepared for each cost center. This type of format can be used, or modified as required, for any specific industry or application.

The data from the Cost Center Worksheet should be transferred to a Weekly Labor & Variable Labor Expense Summary (Figure 4-4). Cost centers are shown as columns on this report. The Maintenance and Steam Departments are considered as service cost centers. These will be distributed back to the productive cost centers in subsequent calculations.

Variable Labor Expense

The rapid rise in labor benefits requires that these expenses be defined and calculated based on standard conditions. These costs should not be based on last year's historical costs. The year-to-year significant changes in the social security base and percent payment is a typical example of errors which can occur using historical results.

In many cases, changes in plant equipment through automation and modification cause an increase or decrease in the number of people required in a particular cost center. This is another case in which the utilization of historical actual cost would result in erroneous estimates of labor benefits.

An example of the calculation of a variable labor expense, social security, is shown in Figure 4-5. This is an example in which the expense varies in a linear manner up to the dollars applicable to social security; then remains constant.

In each case, variable expense accounts should be defined, the basis of calculation listed, and the actual calculation and standard labor conditions recorded. This type of an approach will improve the updating or revision of costs as well as provide the necessary information for cost control. These techniques of calculation are essential for the projection of expected costs for new plants or industrial operations.

All calculations and basic data should be recorded in detail. Many failures of cost revisions or installations are the result of inadequate documentation. Proper records of calculations and data can aid later evaluations, locating errors, and assist with subsequent cost revisions.

In the case of the Dyeing Department, Figure 4-5, a hypothetical example of annual cost of social security is $6,987 per year for the entire department. Yet, the normal operations will be fifty weeks per year. Two weeks of production will normally be lost through vacations, holidays, and other causes. Therefore, the annual costs must be converted to a weekly basis using fifty weeks. The weekly cost to be inserted on the Labor Expense Summary, then, is $6,987 divided by fifty weeks or $140 per week of operation. One job earned in excess of the hypothetical $8,400 base, and resulted in $160 of earnings for which social security was not applicable.

Fifty weeks is used as a normal plant volume, for two weeks of production time are lost by holidays and vacations. Actually, in this example, a third week of production is

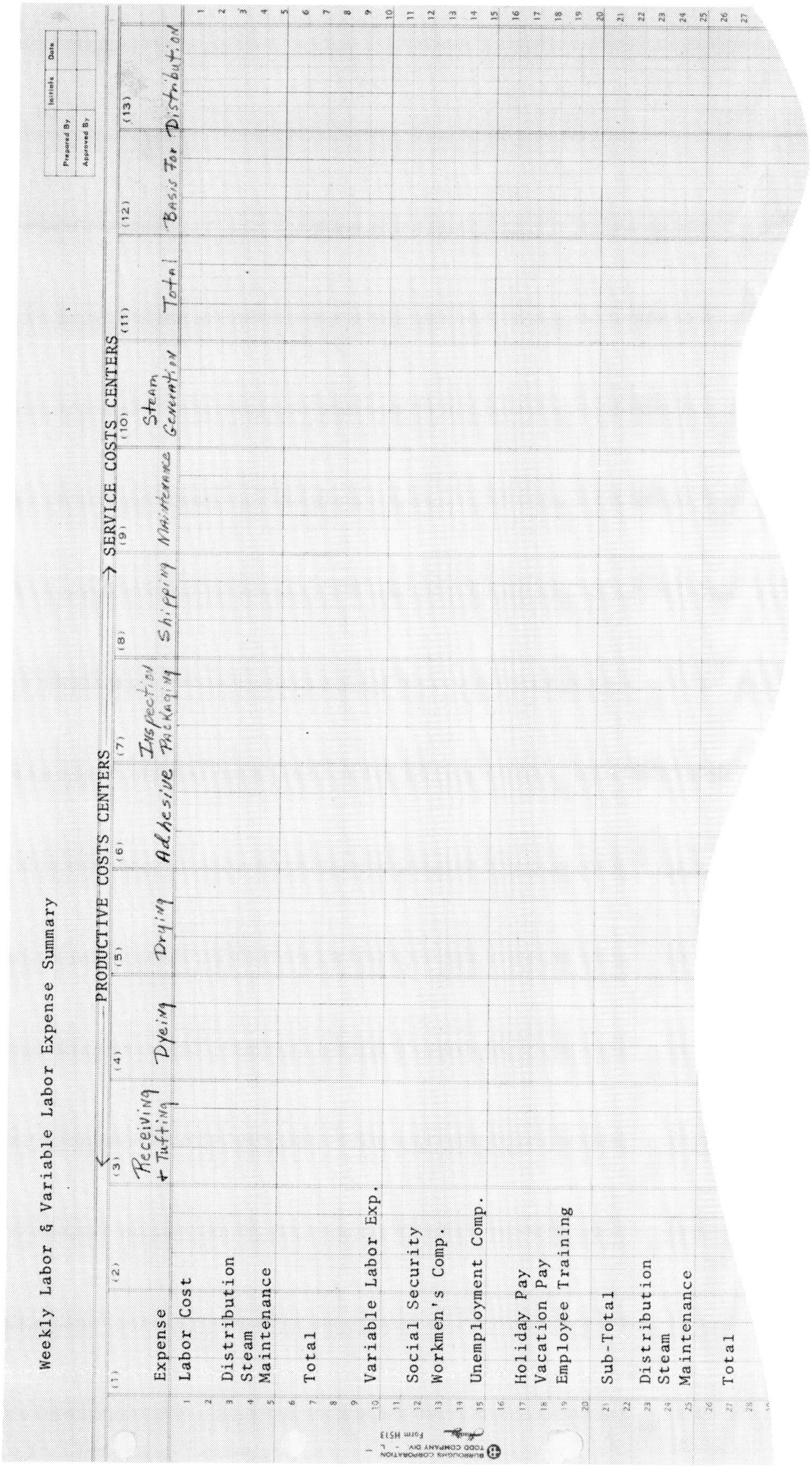

Weekly Labor & Variable Labor Expense Summary

Prepared By	Initials	Date
Approved By		

(1)	(2)	(3)	(4)	(5)	(6)	(7)	(8)	(9)	(10)	(11)	(12)	(13)
		← PRODUCTIVE COSTS CENTERS					→ SERVICE COSTS CENTERS					
Expense		Receiving + Tufting	Dyeing	Drying	Adhesive	Inspection Packaging	Shipping	Maintenance	Steam Generation	Total	Basis for Distribution	
Labor Cost												
Distribution												
Steam												
Maintenance												
Total												
Variable Labor Exp.												
Social Security												
Workmen's Comp.												
Unemployment Comp.												
Holiday Pay												
Vacation Pay												
Employee Training												
Sub-Total												
Distribution												
Steam												
Maintenance												
Total												

Burroughs Corporation Todd Company Div. Form H513

FIGURE 4-4
FORMAT OF LABOR AND VARIABLE EXPENSE SUMMARY

Account Name: FICA

Account Number: 1601

Description of Account:

    Employers share of Social Security costs required

    by Federal Law.

Basis for Calculation:

    5.5 per cent on annual pay up to $8,400, including

vacation and holiday payments.

Dyeing Department

Number of Employees	22
Employee Earnings/Week	$2,400
Weeks Per Year:	
Plant Operation	50
Vacation	2
Holidays	1
Total Paid Weeks	53
Total Earnings Per Year	$127,200
Earnings in Excess of $8,400	- 160
Earnings Applicable to FICA	$127,040
Rate	5.5%
Standard FICA/Year	$ 6,987
Normal Weeks Plant Operation	50
Standard FICA Per Plant Operation Week	$ 140

FIGURE 4-5

VARIABLE LABOR EXPENSE CALCULATION—FICA

recovered by paying personnel to work rather than take a vacation. The weeks of normal volume vary by industry. As vacation and holidays increase, less than fifty weeks of operation can be expected.

    An example of the unemployment compensation insurance calculation is shown in Figure 4-6. These and certain other expenses may vary from year to year based on experience. Therefore, in the years of high employment terminations, the rate may increase whereas in the years of low employee terminations, the rate may decrease. The long-run expected rate or management target should be used on the basis for standard calculations rather than year-to-year historical experience.

Account Name: Unemployment Compensation Insurance

Account Number: 1609

Description of Account:

Payment of State and Federal Unemployment Insurance
Compensation Tax to cover costs of/terminated employees.
(unemployment of)

Basis for Calculation:

1.0 Per cent State and 3.0 Per cent Federal based on
annual pay up to $4,000, including vacation and
holiday payments.

Dyeing Department

Number of Employees	22
Employee Earnings/Week	$2,400
Weeks Per Year: Plant Operations	50
Vacation	2
Holiday	1
Total Paid Weeks	53
Total Earnings Per Year	$127,200
Earnings in Excess of $4,000	-39,200
Earnings Applicable to Unemployment Compensation	$ 88,000
Rate	4.0%
Standard Unemployment	$3,520
Normal Weeks Plant Operation	50
Standard Unemployment Compensation Per Plant Operating Week	$70

FIGURE 4-6

VARIABLE LABOR EXPENSE CALCULATION—UNEMPLOYMENT INSURANCE

In one plant, production disruptions, inadequate scheduling, and other factors caused a high unemployment rate. The management adopted an objective of reducing employee terminations and set out to lower costs in the areas of unemployment compensation, employee training, and related costs. By reflecting these expected improvements in the standard calculations, managers are then in a position to measure their actual performance versus their planned objectives.

Calculations of this type can be developed for most other variable labor expenses. These expenses can, then, be included as shown in Column 4, Figure 4-7, for the Dyeing Department. The example in Figure 4-7 has been completed to include all productive and service cost centers determined in a similar manner.

In past years, receiving, shipping, and other similar functions may have been considered service cost centers. In some instances, these have been placed in a labor expense or fixed cost category. These type cost centers are productive and should be controlled as any other productive department. When they are placed in labor expense or other classifications, these costs may not be controlled effectively.

There are other labor variable expenses for specific industries, firms, or union contracts. Where paid lunch breaks, certain union activities, shift premiums, reporting pay, and others are required, these should be included in the build-up of variable labor expenses. In some cases, these miscellaneous expenses have been included in a miscellaneous or sundry account. This can be misleading and lead to a lack of management control. Every account should be defined and calculated based on expected or planned management objectives. When these accounts do not represent a significant portion of the costs, they may then be combined for reporting purposes.

In all cases, the account title and description should represent the real expense component. The term "sundry" or any other miscellaneous heading should be avoided. In some cases variable labor expenses have been referred to as "burden" or "manufacturing overhead". These are misleading terms which could connote to managers that they cannot be controlled as effectively as labor, materials, or supply parts. *(Note: Any expenditure of money is a cost or an expense; it can and must be controlled—it is not a burden or an overhead.)*

For the example used in this book, the normal operation is eighty hours per week. Therefore, under normal or standard conditions, no overtime would be required. In situations where normal or standard operations require the utilization of an overtime condition, this overtime should be reflected in standard cost. This is particularly important in continuous process industries such as steel refining, synthetic fiber manufacturing, and some chemical industries. This overtime must be planned and calculated based on standard conditions. Then, actual overtime can be controlled against expected standard overtime. The overtime cost should be defined as overtime premium only. The base cost should be shown as normal plant labor cost.

The control of all the various components of manufacturing costs is similar to a balloon. When managers control one element of cost, such as productive labor, often another cost increases on the other side of the balloon. Frequently, the excess cost of overtime premium is the expense which goes out of control, particularly when management concentrates its attention on the number of jobs in a department or plant, rather than total cost reduction.

Weekly Labor & Variable Labor Expense Summary

Prepared By ____ Initials ____ Date ____
Approved By ____

Expense	PRODUCTIVE COSTS CENTERS						SERVICE COSTS CENTERS		Total	Basis for Distribution
	Receiving + Tufting (3)	Dyeing (4)	Drying (5)	Adhesive (6)	Inspection Packing (7)	Shipping (8)	Maintenance (9)	Steam Generation (10)	(11)	(12)
Labor Cost	$9000	$2400	$1500	$2500	$2000	$1100	$1500	$1000	$21000	
Distribution of Service Cost Center Labor Cost										
Steam	100	580	50	120	50	100		(1000)	0	Consumption of Steam
Maintenance	600	200	150	250	200	100	(1500)		0	Utilization of maintenance service
Total	$9700	$3180	$1700	$2870	$2250	$1300	0	0	$21000	
Variable Labor Exp.										
Social Security	$450	$140	$75	$140	$100	$55	$75	50	$1085	
Workmen's Comp.	220	60	40	70	50	25	40	20	525	
Unemployment Comp.	300	70	50	80	70	40	50	40	700	
Holiday Pay	180	50	30	50	40	20	30	20	420	
Vacation Pay	360	100	60	100	80	40	60	40	840	
Employee Training	400	110	75	70	100	50	75	50	930	
Sub-Total	$1910	$530	$330	$510	$440	$230	$330	$220	$4500	
Distribution of Service Cost Center Variable Labor Expense										
Steam	20	140	10	20	10	20		(220)	0	Consumption of Steam
Maintenance	140	40	30	50	40	30	(330)		0	Utilization of maintenance service
Total	$2070	$710	$370	$580	$490	$280	0	0	$4500	

FIGURE 4-7

COMPLETE LABOR AND VARIABLE EXPENSE SUMMARY

Costs Distribution

From an accounting point of view, the first calculation of cost for productive and service cost centers is a primary cost distribution. Now, the cost of service departments must be distributed back to the productive cost centers, as indicated on lines 4, 5, 24, and 25 in Figure 4-7. This is referred to as a secondary distribution.

For each expense, the cause of the cost should be determined and used as a basis for the assignment to cost centers. In the case of steam generation expense, this cause would be steam consumption from meters for process equipment and an estimate of the amount of steam required for heating the building. Sometimes, the square feet of building space heated can be used to distribute the steam utilized for heating. However, this must be done on a rational basis. Warehouses and other areas may not be heated to the level of areas requiring personnel comfort.

An example of the assignment of steam cost is shown in Figure 4-8. In this example, only one cost center requires process steam. Therefore, this cost center should be charged a substantial portion of the cost for generating steam. This is important, for some products may not require processing in this cost center. The use of average cost, or the placing of steam cost into a total expense category would distort the real cost for individual products. Products processed in cost center "B" would be costed too low while those not requiring processing in cost center "B" would be costed too high. Potential errors resulting from averages for expense accounts will be more significant in the cost of fuel, electricity, and others (covered in the next chapter).

Steam Consumption-000 Pounds/Week-Average

Cost Center	Building Heating	Process Equipment	Total Steam	Per Cent
A	25	0	25	5.0
B	0	400	400	80.0
C	15	0	15	3.0
D	15	0	15	3.0
E	25	0	25	5.0
F	20	0	20	4.0
	100	400	500	100.0

FIGURE 4-8
CONSUMPTION OF STEAM

Where meters and other engineered controls are available, the application of steam and similar expenses can be considered as direct rather than a distribution. This will improve real cost determination and usually eliminate the questions or criticisms arising from cost distributions.

The cost per machine hour or machine hour rates developed in Figure 4-9 and subsequent calculations will be used to compile the manufacturing cost for application to cost sheets. With these data, the Cost Center Worksheet can be expanded to include service departments and variable labor benefits, also shown in Figure 4-9.

Labor Cost Control

A typical labor weekly Cost Control Report is shown in Figure 4-10. The *individual* job data may be on a weekly basis with twelve-week accumulations. The *variable* labor benefits may be included on the twelve-week accumulations only. These expenses would not be valid for management decisions and actions on a weekly basis. Often, holiday and vacation pay does not occur continuously. Therefore, these costs would be included as they occur for control purposes.

The data in Figure 4-10 indicates that one holiday occurred during the twelve-week-to-date accumulation. Apparently, some employees were not eligible for holiday pay. Therefore a variance gain of $80 occurred. Consequently, no vacation pay occurred during this time interval, resulting in no allowed standard or actual cost for vacation pay.

In some instances where vacation and holiday pay is guaranteed by seniority or employment contract, these are fixed expenses for the short term. Otherwise, these are variable for hourly employees and fixed for salary employees.

In some firms, a relative portion of holiday, vacation, and similar payments are accrued on a monthly basis for Budget Control Statements. Accruals or other similar techniques of this type reduce the effectiveness of budget control and should be avoided wherever practical. Variable budgeting techniques with cost on an *as occurred* basis provide management the best opportunity for management control.

Certain fringe benefits, such as unemployment compensation can be controlled by managers. This may require the control of production to stabilize employment, rather than periodically increasing or decreasing employment. Fluctuation in employment levels increases unemployment compensation and resulting insurance rates.

A four-week time period, with thirteen four-week periods per year, provides a good time basis for cost control reporting. Calendar months, quarters, or periods with four and five weeks or other inconsistent time intervals reduces the effectiveness of cost control. Reports with accumulations in excess of eight to twelve weeks are too insensitive to change to indicate a real improvement or increase in cost performance.

For cost control reports similar to Figure 4-10, the actual cost is taken from payroll records. The standard cost is calculated from output production reports. An example of the standard cost calculation for the Dye Weigher (see Figure 4-2) in the Dyeing Department is as follows (on page 90):

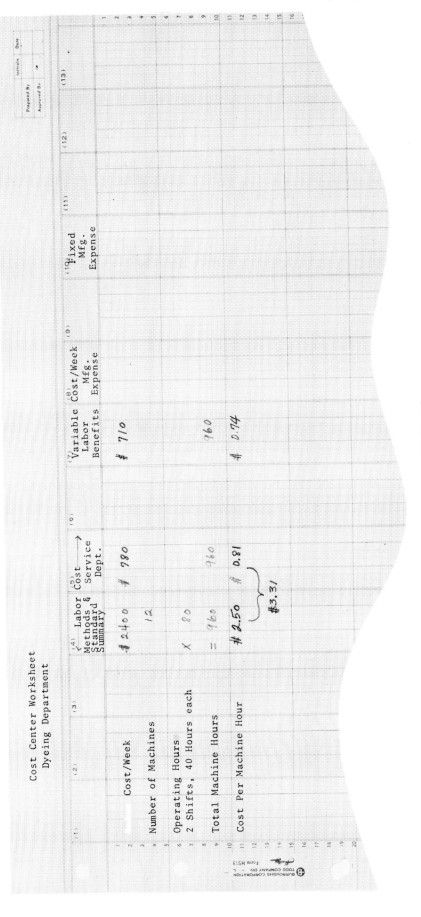

FIGURE 4-9

SEMI-COMPLETE COST CENTER WORKSHEET

DYEING DEPARTMENT

	COST ITEM	WEEK ENDING: XX-XX-XX			12 WEEKS TO DATE		
		STANDARD $	ACTUAL $	VARIANCE $	STANDARD $	ACTUAL $	VARIANCE $
LABOR AND OVERTIME	DYER						
	DYE WEIGHER	250	260	(10)			
	OPERATORS						
	LOADERS						
	CLERK						
	OVERTIME PREMIUM						
VARIABLE LABOR EXPENSE	SOCIAL SECURITY	XXX	XXX	XXX			
	WORKMEN'S COMPENSATION	X	X	X			
	UNEMPLOYMENT COMPENSATION	X	X	X			
	HOLIDAY PAY	X	X	X	480	400	80
	VACATION PAY	X	X	X	0	0	0
	EMPLOYEE TRAINING	X	X	X			
	SUB-TOTAL	XXXX	XXX	XXX			
	TOTAL						

FIGURE 4-10
LABOR COST CONTROL REPORT

Product Number	Output Production	Standard Cost/100 SY	Total Standard Cost
201	100,000	0.163	$163
619	25,000	0.216	54
990	10,000	0.325	33
		Total	$250

The standard cost is compared to the actual cost in Figure 4-10. A loss of ($10) is indicated. This report will be expanded to include all costs controllable by a department manager as these are developed in a later chapter.

Where data processing equipment is available, labor cost control reports can be published weekly by shift, daily by shift, or at other desired time intervals. These more timely reports provide management with the ultimate opportunity for prompt and effective decisions and actions to reduce and maintain costs control.

SUMMARY

The determination and control of labor cost can be the difference between a profit or a loss in those industries where labor costs is a large part of total costs.

Labor cost includes payment direct to employees as well as vacation pay, holiday pay, social security, and other related expenses.

Some expenses are direct or vary as production operations change. Others are fixed and, therefore, do not vary with time or volume of operation. Classification of these expenses is explained in this chapter.

The separation of labor into direct and indirect categories is discarded in favor of the term productive labor. The expenditure of any business resource is productive and should be controlled, or it should be eliminated.

Labor cost should be determined by Methods and Standards engineers' calculations, or the best management estimates. Cost calculation and cost control by historical averages leads to incorrect decisions and failure to attain competitive performance.

Once cost for both productive and service departments has been accumulated, the service department cost should be assigned directly or distributed on a rational basis to productive cost centers. Then, the cost may be calculated for individual products or items, and controlled by reports on a weekly, daily, shift, or other desired time interval.

Variable manufacturing and fixed manufacturing expenses will be evaluated in the next chapter.

CHAPTER FIVE

Evaluating Manufacturing Expenses

Manufacturing expenses exceed labor cost in many industrial operations. Often, those responsible for cost control have concentrated on determining and controlling labor cost, and may leave other manufacturing expenses to the general accountant.

Manufacturing expenses are sometimes called conversion cost. Conversion cost, which includes labor cost, are those costs necessary to convert raw and in-process materials into a finished product for packaging and sale. Conversion cost may also be those costs incurred in converting materials to a semi-finished state for subsequent processing by another division of the firm or a customer.

Manufacturing expenses are classified as variable and fixed using the logic described for separating labor cost into variable and fixed calculations in Chapter Four. Variable expenses include operating supplies, fuel, electricity, water, and others which may be necessary for a particular firm or industry. Fixed expenses include salaries for managers and supervisors, social security for salaried employees, depreciation, and others. The costs for manufacturing service departments, including personnel, methods and standards, and similar services, are fixed expenses. Insurance and property taxes on manufacturing facilities, pension and hospitalization programs, employee training, building maintenance and repair, and similar costs are likewise fixed expenses.

Variable Manufacturing Expenses

Variable manufacturing expenses are controllable by managers. These expenses must be calculated and controlled as the level of plant operation changes equally as effectively as labor cost must be controlled.

Sometimes, budgets or standard costs for variable manufacturing expenses have been determined from last year's historical cost. For effective cost control, these expenses must be calculated based on standard conditions. The accumulation of these expenses into a total account and the distribution of this total to cost centers is obsolete.

Calculations based on engineering specifications and standard conditions are essential for new installations. As an example, a gas-fired piece of process equipment is designed to operate at a given speed, say to produce 75 feet per minute of dry laminates at a temperature of 200°F. The manufacturer of the equipment obtains the contract based on a design with insulation and controls to consume 5,000,000 BTU's of natural gas per hour of operation. The standard cost for gas should be determined by *Standard Gas Consumption × Gas Cost per 100 Cubic Feet = Cost per Machine Hour of Operation,* or:

5,000,000 BTU's of 1,000 BTU/Cubic Foot Gas = 5,000 Cubic Feet/Hour
5,000 Cubic Feet/Hour × $1.00/100 Cubic Feet = $50.00

With this method, actual cost can be compared with standard. Then, when a variance occurs, an engineering investigation can determine the cause of the gain or loss. It may be that the manufacturer did not conform to specifications, and a modification to the equipment, at the contractor's expense, may be required. In another case, the natural gas may not be delivered at the specified contract BTU's per cubic foot. Or, engineers may locate losses in piping or other areas which would improve the cost of operation.

Proper control of utilities requires meters to measure consumption at major points of usage. In some situations, it may not be economical or feasible to have adequate meters. In these cases, utility cost should be accumulated in total and distributed to cost centers on the best engineering estimate.

In most situations, variable manufacturing expenses can and must be calculated based on standard conditions for effective cost control. Calculated standards permit managers to concentrate on the cause of cost and eliminate the errors caused when these expenses are accumulated in total and then distributed or allocated to cost centers.

Operating Supplies and Repairs

Operating supplies and repairs are those expense components of machinery, equipment, or building which are used in routine operations. These include gears, motor parts, lubricants, and similar items.

Expense items are those costs which are charged to the operation, either into inventory or consumption, upon purchase. Capital expenditures are those purchases of equipment, building, or machinery which are depreciable. The determination of capital or expense must be consistent with internal revenue codes. Operating supplies are generally expense items.

One definition of capital and expense items is included in Figure 5-1. Management's policy, definitions, and descriptions should be documented in the form of a policy and instructions. These types of communications are essential to insure proper and consistent reporting, and classification of supply and repair costs in plants and between plants or divisions.

To supplement these policies and instructions, Supply Cost Specifications, similar to Figure 5-2, should be developed. These should include a listing of the parts with a high proportion of the costs. The standards should be related to the output production unit in the department, either machine hours, revolutions, linear measurement, or other reporting unit.

For standard purposes, a standard process condition must be selected. Yet, for control purposes, a standard speed of equipment for each process condition may be required. Sometimes, different plants will operate similar equipment at different speeds. Those with higher speeds may have a different supply cost standard. Where machine hours are used as the basic costing unit, standards should reflect the difference in speeds and processing conditions.

Wherever practical, operating supply and maintenance cost standards should be calculated based on expected replacement cycles, an analysis of breakdown studies, engineering studies and analyses. As an example, one department may be using a roll covering which must be replaced every 5,000 hours. The formula for calculating the cost would be:

$$\frac{\text{Number of Rolls}}{\text{Life in Machine Hours}} \times \begin{array}{c}\text{Cost Per Roll Covered,}\\ \text{including cost of}\\ \text{machine downtime}\end{array} = \begin{array}{c}\text{Cost Per}\\ \text{Machine Hour}\end{array}$$

In cases where significant costs are involved, statistical analysis and probability theory may aid in the determination of the optimum replacement cycle. This is particularly true where the replacement cost of a roller by a maintenance employee may be substantially higher than a planned group replacement costs of rollers. The same would hold true for light bulb replacement.

For control purposes where group replacement is used, or actual maintenance is on a cycle basis—say every six months—the allowed standard must reflect these cycles, rather than an allowance per machine hour. Periodically, such frequency allowances must be balanced with standard machine hour rates.

With calculations of this type, it is possible for managers to find out the cause of variances. Possibly, the roll covering was not performing satisfactorily or the manufacturing department was changing the covering too frequently.

This approach requires engineers and managers to evaluate the cause of supply cost —equipment speed, age of equipment, product manufactured, and others, rather than employ historical cost records. Specifications of this type provide the basic data for cost calculation, cost control, and equipment replacement decisions.

Normally, machine hours determined from process conditions and speed will be utilized for standard cost calculations. Revolutions, linear measurements, or applicable net output production units for given operations or departments are used for allowing standard cost. The net output production for the related operation is multipled by the standard cost per net output unit to give the allowed standard cost for comparison to actual cost.

At every step, for every expense from initial specifications through material loss, supplies, and others, a specification based on standard conditions should be prepared and

POLICY AND JOB INSTRUCTIONS	Title: OPERATING SUPPLY AND REPAIR COSTS REPORTING & CONTROL POLICY

GENERAL POLICY STATEMENT

In today's competitive industry, it is essential that supply and repair costs be reported correctly and reduced to a minimum consistent with proper maintenance of equipment.

It is essential that equipment be maintained for optimum cost operation. Inadequate maintenance and below standard expenditures are as undesirable as excess costs.

Expenditures are classified as capital or expense.
(a) Capital expenditures are any item or component of machinery, equipment, or building with a cost in excess of $100 and a useful life in excess of one year.
(b) Expense expenditures are items or components which cost $100 or less and have a useful life of one year or less, or a routine expendable item of equipment, repair, or supply used or consumed in the manufacturing process.

Supply and repair costs are defined as:
(a) Machinery maintenance supplies are those items replaced due to wear in routine operations of equipment. These include machine parts, gears, drives, and other items of machinery and equipment from the motor forward through the machine. This includes shop supplies used in equipment maintenance and repairs.
(b) General supplies are those operating supplies not normally utilized in machinery maintenance. These include tape, brooms, light bulbs, and others.
(c) Building repairs are those items used in repair and maintenance of building and building equipment up to, but not including, the motor.
(d) Process carriers are those items used to move material from process to process or within a process. These include trucks, cans, conveyors, and others.
(e) Product change parts are those items which must be replaced due to change in products or designs. These may include patterns, molds, certain machine parts, and others.
(f) Materials handling supply and repair parts are those items for conveyors, lift trucks, elevators and other similar handling equipment.

(g) Major items of machine parts with a life over one year for periodic overhauling of machinery and equipment shall be on a budget basis. These are not a part of the routine supply and repair costs.

No person may obtain any item without an approved requisition. The limits of requisition approval authority are:

Department Manager - Up to $250
Superintendent - $250 to $2,500
Plant Manager - $2,500 to $5,000
Vice President - $5,000 or over

Issued By:	Approved By:	Superceded Date	Effective Date:	No. 440.1
		None	xx-xx-xx	

FIGURE 5-1
OPERATING SUPPLY AND REPAIR COSTS REPORTING
AND CONTROL POLICY

historical conditions avoided. Effective management, cost control, and production planning rests on the foundation of engineered specifications.

Fuel, Electricity, and Utilities

Fuel, electricity, and other utility costs should be determined for the normal volume production and standard conditions.

Calculations are particularly important in evaluating new facilities and plant sites. Industries which utilize a high volume of heated water may find a significant difference in cost between locations based on the difference between the input water and heated level required. Heating water in cold climates, as well as heating for personnel comfort, can be significantly higher than those for warmer climates. These factors can be important when estimating cost for new plants or in comparing operating cost differences between existing plants.

Electricity cost may be calculated as illustrated in Figure 5-3. Standard cost calculations of this type can highlight variances from actual cost. A detailed, engineering cost study can determine the cause of the variance and permit management to make decisions and take actions. In the case of electricity, the power factor may be low, motors may be operating below an efficient load, start-up power loads may result in a demand charge which could be lowered by varying the start-up time of departments, or motors and lights may simply not be cut off when operations are not in progress. Effective management requires a blending of engineering and cost data.

Account Code	Description	Basis of Calculation	Cost Per Output Unit
21	Roller Covering	$\dfrac{\text{Number of Rollers}}{\text{Replacement Cycle}} \times \begin{array}{c}\text{Standard Cost}\\ \text{Per Cover}\end{array}$	$ 0.040
22	Aprons	$\dfrac{\text{Number of Aprons}}{\text{Replacement Cycle}} \times \begin{array}{c}\text{Standard Cost}\\ \text{Per Apron}\end{array}$	0.025
24	Belts	$\dfrac{\text{Number of Belts}}{\text{Expected Belt Life}} \times \begin{array}{c}\text{Standard Cost}\\ \text{Per Belt}\end{array}$	0.015
25	Lubricants	Lubrication Study	0.012
26	Motors & Drive Repairs	Engineering Analysis	0.028
27	Light Bulbs	$\dfrac{\text{Number of Bulbs}}{\text{Replacement Cycle}} \times \begin{array}{c}\text{Standard}\\ \text{Cost Per Bulb}\end{array}$	0.007
28	Other Parts & Supplies	Costs Analysis of Usage	0.008
	Standard Cost Per Million Revolutions		$ 0.135

Issued by:	Approved by:	Department Spinning	Effective Date xx-xx-xx	No. 399

FIGURE 5-2
SUPPLY AND REPAIR COST SPECIFICATION

	Tufting Receiving	Dyeing	Drying	Adhesive	Inspection & Packing	Shipping	Maint. Supply	Steam Generation	Total
Horsepower	280	100	350	200	40	20	100	40	
Kilowatt (KW)*	210	75	260	150	30	15	75	30	
Running Hours/Week	80	80	80	80	80	80	80	80	
% Run Time	50	75	90	90	50	50	25	100	
Total KW/Wk.	8,400	4,500	18,800	10,800	1,200	600	1,500	2,400	
Lighting	9,000	6,000	1,500	2,000	2,550	6,100	1,000	950	
KW/Week	17,400	10,500	20,300	12,800	3,750	6,700	2,500	3,350	
Cost/KW	$0.012	$0.012	$0.012	$0.012	$0.012	$0.012	$0.012	$0.012	
Cost/Week*	$210	$125	$245	$155	$45	$80	$30	$40	930
Cost/50 Week Year	$10,500	$6,250	$12,250	$7,750	$2,250	$4,000	$1,500	$2,000	$46,500

* = Rounded to 5 increment

FIGURE 5-3

CALCULATION OF ELECTRIC POWER COST

Fixed Manufacturing Expense

Fixed manufacturing expenses, though not controllable as levels of plant operation change, are either influenced by management decisions or controllable on a financial budget.

Managers need to consider the effect of depreciation on financial operating results when evaluating new plants, equipment, or modifications. An example of an incomplete manufacturing expense worksheet is shown in Figure 5-4. Variable expenses for the Dyeing Department have been inserted.

Salaries for the manufacturing and department managers may be obtained from the Salary Budget, similar to Figure 2-7. Fixed social security, and other payroll taxes including workmen's compensation insurance and unemployment compensation can be calculated in a manner similar to that developed for those expenses in labor cost. A cost report for the Methods and Standards Department, Personnel Department, and other manufacturing service departments may be prepared as shown in Figure 5-5. Where data processing and more extensive accounting systems are in operation, other charges not shown in Figure 5-5 can be easily included in the department's expense budget.

Depreciation

Depreciation is that amount of money which must be recovered for utilization and replacement of equipment and buildings, resulting from capital expenditures.

A Depreciation Cost Worksheet for the Dyeing Department is shown in Figure 5-6. All major items of equipment should be listed separately. The key elements of information are the current replacement value and expected life. In some cases, adjustments must be made for salvage value at the end of the expected life.

The value per unit should be the replacement value in the market for the given year of the cost or industrial planning system. In past years, some firms have used the actual cost value for these assets which may result in the loss of sunk cost in an inflationary economy. Inflation has become such an important factor that all values for depreciation in business planning and pricing should be adjusted for current or expected value. Should a planning system be estimating profits or prices in future years, say five years ahead, the values for depreciation should be adjusted for expected price increases in the next five years.

The use of replacement values is suggested for management planning. External financial reporting and tax accounting must conform to accepted accounting practice and government regulations. Sometimes, accelerated depreciation methods are utilized, though there is a trend back to straight line depreciation calculations.

Replacement values are necessary to determine the investment in current dollars. As will be shown later, this total replacement value will be considered the investment from which the standard profit will be determined.

For new installations, the replacement value is readily available. Where older equipment is involved, the value should be for equipment with the same production capability.

Variable:	Cost Per 80 Hour Week	Cost Per 50 Week Year
Operating Supplies	$ 600	$ 30,000
Fuel & Gas	2,700	135,000
Water	415	20,750
Electricity	125	6,250
Sub-Total: Variable	$ 3,840	$192,000

Fixed:

Manufacturing Managers

Department Managers

Fixed Social Security,
  & Other Payroll Taxes

Depreciation

Methods & Standards Dept.

Personnel Department

Insurance

Property Tax

Salary & Pension Plan

Hospital & Major Medical Program

Building Maintenance & Repair

Sub-Total: Fixed

     TOTAL

FIGURE 5-4

MANUFACTURING EXPENSE WORKSHEET—DYEING DEPARTMENT

Even though automated and more sophisticated equipment may be available, the cost for these advanced machines should not be used. The more modern equipment will require less labor or other expenses and a higher investment. Many texts have covered the techniques of valuing equipment for depreciation and many accountants have discussed

Methods & Standards Department Expense

Description of Expense	Cost Per Week	Cost Per Year
Chief, Methods & Standards Department	$ 320	$ 16,000
Methods & Standards Engineers (2)	500	25,000
Methods & Standards Technicians (1)	200	10,000
Print Shop Charges	20	1,000
Office Equipment	35	1,750
Office Space Charge	25	1,250
Travel & Seminar Expense	30	1,500
Professional Dues & Subscriptions	5	250
Other Expenses	65	3,250
Total:	$1,200	$ 60,000

FIGURE 5-5

MANUFACTURING SERVICE DEPARTMENT EXPENSE BUDGET

Description	No. of Machines or Sq.Ft.	Replacement Value Per Unit	Total Replacement Value	Expected Life	Depreciation Per Year (Rounded to $100)	Total Replacement Value	Total Depreciation
DYEING DEPARTMENT							
Dye Becks W/Process Control	12	30,000	360,000	10	36,000		
Sample & Lab. Equipment	-	25,000	25,000	10	2,500		
Misc. Equipment	-	50,000	50,000	10	5,000	815,000	54,500
Building Inc. Storage	30,000	12	360,000	40	9,000		
Storage Racks	-	20,000	20,000	10	2,000		

FIGURE 5-6

CALCULATION OF REPLACEMENT VALUE DEPRECIATION

the subject in detail. Some criticisms of replacement value may be valid. Yet, where inflation is an important factor, and where the business is to be in operation for the long run, replacement of facilities will be required. Then, replacement value costing and return on replacement value investment pricing will provide the best guide for planning and product evaluation.

In specialized pricing decisions in declining markets or for technological advantages, the application of depreciation may be altered. The handling of these specialized situations for pricing is covered in Chapter Nine, "Pricing for Growth and Profit."

One problem from an accounting standpoint in using replacement value is that the planned depreciation will not be the same as the book value charged to financial statements for tax purposes. This difference or variance must be adjusted for inventory pricing for tax purposes. With existing accelerated depreciation methods including sum of years digits, declining balance, and other acceptable accounting methods or replacement value depreciation, it is virtually impossible to utilize a value in standard cost which is identical to the value charged into financial results. This results in two accounts —one for tax purposes, and one for standard cost. The difference can be included as a variance between standard profit and actual profit in internal management control reports.

The first objective of the standard costing and industrial planning system is to provide information for management decisions and control based on management objectives. Inventory pricing may be a secondary consideration.

On occasions, financial managers may be so concerned with the reduction of income taxes that the information provided management is not in a form for objective analysis, decisions, and actions. The real facts about the business health must be reported to managers. These facts must not be concealed in the interest of reducing income taxes or other factors.

Replacement values are necessary for making plant to plant comparisons of cost. Should a plant comparison be made with an older plant with low net book value, and a new plant with a high book value with accelerated depreciation, the new plant would appear to have a higher total cost, when, in fact, the reverse would be true. Where factors which are not consistent are present, plant to plant comparisons may be valid only on the variable cost elements.

Regardless of the method of depreciation utilized in standard costing, planning, and financial statements, it is essential for managers to understand the calculations and their effect on financial results.

Depreciation added to after-tax profit is cash flow, the amount of money returning to the business in cash for investment, repayment of loans, or expansion.

The expected life of assets may be determined from the estimated useful life of the equipment or building, or technological obsolescence. For income tax and external financial reporting, internal revenue codes are required. Yet, for standard costing and industrial planning, the estimated useful life should be the basis. Wherever the equipment will become technologically obsolete in a time interval shorter than the useful life, the reduced technological life of the equipment should be used for planning. With the rapid advancements in automated and advanced technology, managers may need to recover the cost and plan to replace equipment and facilities well before the useful life of the equipment is reached.

The depreciation calculations for the example in Figure 5-6 are on a straightline method of depreciation, or the equivalent of an equal amount of depreciation for each year of the expected life.

Other Fixed Manufacturing Expenses

Salary continuation and pension programs, hospitalization and major medical insurance plans, and other similar expenses should be defined, and the basis for calculation determined. The budget then, should be calculated based on standard conditions. Normally, these expenses may be on a calculated cost per employee, for which the program is applicable, multiplied by the number of applicable employees.

Building maintenance and repair expenses which include the painting of buildings, replacement of floors, and building equipment expenses may be in total. This expense may be distributed to cost centers on a basis of square feet of floor space utilized for the cost center.

Using similar techniques, the cost for the other cost centers in this example can be completed as indicated in Figure 5-7. In this example, the Methods and Standards and Personnel Departments have been distributed to the cost centers based on the standard number of employees in each cost center for normal operations. On some occasions, accountants have used the number of actual employees on the payroll. This basis could be misleading for some departments may have excess employees for various reasons. For the same reason, all calculations of expenses for labor must be based on the standard number of employees or standard labor dollars, not the existing conditions or historical results.

The service cost centers may be distributed to the productive cost centers in the same manner that variable labor costs were distributed in Chapter Four. These data can be inserted in the cost center worksheets and machine hour rates calculated as shown in Figure 5-8.

The calculation of machine hour costs are to slide rule accuracy. Normally, two or three significant numbers are satisfactory. Excessive decimal points and carrying the cost per week to dollars or pennies is unnecessary.

The costs per machine hour for the Dyeing Department are:

Costs		Cost Per Machine Hour
Methods & Standards Labor Summary		$ 2.50
Service Departments		.81
Sub-Total—Labor		$ 3.31
Variable Labor Benefits		$ .74
Variable Manufacturing Expense		4.17
Sub-Total—Variable Costs		$ 8.22
Fixed Manufacturing Expense		$ 2.96
	Total	$11.18

Annual Manufacturing Expense Summary

(1) Expense	(2) Receiving & Tufting	(4) Dyeing	(5) Drying	(6) Adhesive	(7) Inspection & Packing	(8) Shipping	(9) Maint.	(10) Steam Generation	(11) Total	(12) Basis
Variable Manufacturing Expense:										
Operating Supplies	$40000	$30000	$7500	$5000	$5000	$7500	$11500	$5000	$111500	Supply Specifications
Fuel & Gas	8000	135000	22000	25000	2000	6000	2000	–	200000	Steam Consumption Analysis
Water	–	20750	–	1250	–	4000	–	3000	25000	Direct Charge
Electricity	10500	6250	12250	7750	2250	4000	1500	2000	46500	Direct Charge
Sub-Total: Variable	$58500	$192000	$41750	$39000	$9250	$17500	$15000	$10000	$383000	
Distribution										
Steam	$1000	$6000	$500	$1000	$500	$1000	–	($10000)	0	Steam Consumption
Maintenance	6000	2600	1500	2500	2000	1000	(15000)	0	0	Utilization of Maint. Svcs.
Total/Year	$65500	$200600	$43750	$42500	$11750	$19500	0	0	$383000	
Total/Week	$1310	$4000	$875	$850	$235	$390	0	0	$7660	
Fixed Manufacturing Expense:										
Manufacturing Mgrs.	$12000	$10000	$5000	$12000	$12000	$12000	$12000	–	$75000	Department Managers
Dept. Managers	12000	10000	5000	12000	12000	12000	12000	–	75000	Direct Charge
Fixed Soc. Security & other Payroll Taxes	1600	1200	400	1600	1600	1600	1600	–	9600	Department Managers
Depreciation	135500	54500	20000	25000	20000	35000	21150	18250	329400	Direct Calculation
Methods & Stds. Dpt.	39000	11000	6000	–	–	–	–	4000	60000	Number of Employees
Personnel Dept.	–	–	–	9000	9000	11000	6000	–	35000	Number of Employees
Insurance	12000	6000	1500	3000	3000	15000	1500	–	42000	Building & Equipment Replacement Value
Property Tax	1500	1000	500	500	500	1000	500	250	5750	"
Salary & Pension Plan	25000	12500	5000	5000	5000	15000	6000	4000	77500	Direct Calculation
Hospital & Major Medical Program	5000	1500	750	1250	1250	1500	750	500	12500	"
Building Maintenance	30000	8000	4000	6000	6000	8000	4000	2500	68500	$0.20 x Square Feet
Sub-Total: Fixed	$273600	$115700	$48150	$75350	$70350	$112100	$65000	$30000	$790250	
Distribution										
Steam	$3000	$18000	$1500	$3000	$1500	$3000	–	($30000)	0	Steam Consumption
Maintenance	26000	8500	6500	11000	9000	4000	($65000)	–	0	Utilization of Maint. Svcs.
Total/Year	$302600	$142200	$56150	$89350	$80850	$119100	0	0	$790250	
Total/Week	$6052	$2844	$1123	$1787	$1617	$2382	0	0	$15805	

(13) Prepared By _____ Approved By _____ Initials / Date

Form HS13 — TODD COMPANY DIV., BURROUGHS CORPORATION

FIGURE 5-7
MANUFACTURING EXPENSE SUMMARY

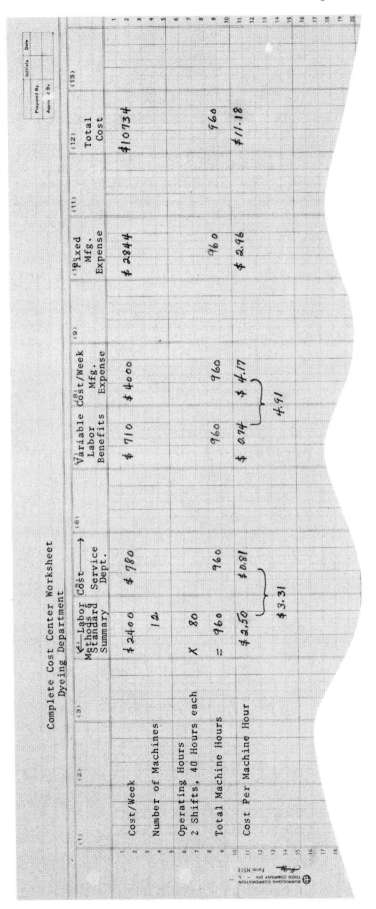

FIGURE 5-8

COMPLETE COST CENTER WORKSHEET

The total cost per machine hour, or in the case of the Dyeing Department, per dye-beck hour, is $11.18. For each dyebeck hour used by a product, it is necessary to recover $11.18 in standard cost to recover the total cost of the Dyeing Department.

In variable or direct costing, machine hour rates may be calculated for variable expenses only, with fixed expenses handled separately. This technique and its resulting effect on profitability analysis, cost control, and inventory pricing shall be discussed in more detail in subsequent chapters.

In the example of Figure 5-8 for the Dyeing Department, the fixed cost per machine hour is $2.96 based on two shift operation with twelve machines, or 960 machine hours per week. This normal operating level was determined from management's policy statement or objective. It is related to competitive conditions within the industry.

The determination of normal volume is extremely important in total cost calculations involving fixed costs. If a one shift operation had been selected in this example, the fixed costs per machine hour would be:

Fixed cost per week	$2,844
Number of Machines	12
Operating hours per week	40
Total machine hours per week	480
Cost per machine hour	$ 5.94

Often, manufacturing expenses may be based on a derived practical plant capacity, or an expected plant utilization based on the sales forecast. There is some merit to each of these bases provided managers understand the effect of the basis on the total cost calculations. The basis selected should be based on a management decision related to the competitive, as well as industry and management's objectives. The cost accountant may recommend a particular basis and point out the effect of various bases. Often, the basis selected may be more related to the practical business situation, rather than to conform to accounting theory.

In some cases, the sales volume budget may be used as a basis. This objective is suspect. For manufacturing expenses, the machine hour rates should be based on the ability to produce, rather than the ability to sell. The difference is a volume or idle capacity gain or loss.

In most cases, regardless of the basis selected, there will be idle capacity in the total plant. Similarly, the product mix may not balance in all departments, leaving idle capacity in individual cost centers. The handling of idle capacity costs will be discussed as it affects decisions.

The reduction of idle capacity losses is a management opportunity. Market prices cannot be altered simply because of variances in actual as compared to standard volume.

In most industrial situations involving machinery, the cost per machine hour for manufacturing expense is the best basis. In past years, these expenses have been applied as a percent of direct labor, in some instances. The utilization of direct labor as the basis shall fail to point up real differences in cost by product.

The operating supplies, electricity, and other similar items may vary directly with production machine hours. One product may require a machine crew of four, and for another product a crew of two may be adequate. Should variable manufacturing expenses or fixed manufacturing expenses be applied for standard purposes as a percent of direct labor, the product with a crew of two would be costed below real cost and the product with a crew of four would be costed excessively.

Another basis which may be considered is the cost per unit passing through a cost center. In some cases this basis may be satisfactory. However, where machinery or equipment is involved, and the product mix or time requirements of a product in a cost center vary significantly, the cost per unit basis is an average cost. Cost per unit will not reflect variations in real costs within the product mix.

In some instances, the material cost passing through a cost center is a basis for applying manufacturing expenses. In most cases, this is unsatisfactory. Items with a low material costs content will be costed at a low level whereas items with a high material costs content will be costed substantially higher. In some cases, the higher cost material will pass through a cost center faster and with less utilization of machine hours. *The utilization of material cost as a basis for applying manufacturing expenses to standard cost must be evaluated very carefully.*

Manufacturing managers would often like to run a simplified product line with few products, colors, or variations. In firms manufacturing industrial products, this may be feasible. In consumer products, however, the ever increasing need to satisfy the desires of "Mr." and "Mrs." Consumer may require an increasingly complex product line. As product and production needs become more complex, managers must insist on a cost control and profit planning system which develops the real costs by product rather than techniques which reflect average conditions.

Cost Control of Manufacturing Expense

All controllable cost for the cost centers should be placed on one statement for the department or plant manager. Earlier, a cost control statement for labor costs was developed. This can be expanded to include manufacturing expense as illustrated in Figure 5-9.

This example is for a department within a plant. Similar statements for the total plant can be prepared by summarizing all the departments or cost centers. This type of statement permits the manager to have before him on one statement all the elements of manufacturing costs for which he is responsible and can control. Often, managers receive a labor cost statement from the Methods and Standards Department, a variable cost statement from accounting, and then fixed cost control reports either from the Budget Department or as part of the financial statements.

Effective control of the cost control balloon requires the manager to get one statement showing all elements of costs. This permits the manager to ask the important questions about his department or staff: "Why did we have a gain in operating supplies?", or "What caused the excessive variance due to overtime?". Detailed analysis of these gains and losses permits the department managers to find the cause of these variances, and take action to correct the situation.

Though cost statements may be on a daily, weekly, or four-week time schedule,

DYEING DEPARTMENT

	COST ITEM	WEEK ENDING: XX-XX-XX			12 WEEKS TO DATE		
		STANDARD $	ACTUAL $	VARIANCE $	STANDARD $	ACTUAL $	VARIANCE $
L A B O R	**DIRECT** DYER						
	DYE WEIGHER	250	260	(10)			
	AND OPERATORS						
	OVERTIME LOADERS						
	CLERK						
	OVERTIME PREMIUM						
VARIABLE EXPENSE MFG	OPERATING SUPPLIES						
	FUEL AND GAS	2,700	2,550	150			
	WATER						
	ELECTRICITY						
VARIABLE LABOR EXPENSE	SOCIAL SECURITY	XXX	XXX	XXX			
	WORKMEN'S COMPENSATION	X	X	X			
	UNEMPLOYMENT COMPENSATION	X	X	X			
	HOLIDAY PAY	X	X	X	480	400	80
	VACATION PAY	X	X	X	0	0	0
	EMPLOYEE TRAINING	XXX	XXX	XXX			
	TOTAL						

FIGURE 5-9
DEPARTMENT COST CONTROL REPORT

managers may wish to have a bi-weekly meeting of their department managers or shift foremen. Often, Methods and Standards Engineers should be included in these meetings to review performance for the past time period.

For each significant loss, managers should insist that their staff personnel and line management prepare a list of the problems, the changes or corrections required, the persons responsible, and a date for completion or follow-up as indicated in Figure 5-10.

An analysis of this type requires that all causes of cost variances be reviewed. Often, action is required by a particular department to improve the performance of a subsequent department. Interpersonnel relations are likely to become strained unless an open, candid approach is taken by all involved in the improvement of organization performance.

Dyeing Department

Problem	Factors Affecting Cost	Correction	Responsible Person	Target Date	Follow-up
Below Standard Production Per Machine Hour	1. Below Standard Roll Length	1. Increase Roll Length in Tufting	Tufting Manager		
	2. Off-quality requiring redyeing/overstandard	2. Better control of water Ph, and dye weighing	Quality Control Manager		
	3. Temperature difference from input water to dye temperature level.	3. Install additional and faster water heating units	Mechanical Engineering		
	4. Employee turnover in Beck Control Operator	4. Re-evaluate job	Personnel Manager		

FIGURE 5-10
COST IMPROVEMENT PROGRAM

Effective cost control and competitive performance is obtained by all departments and people working together on the same drive shaft. Cost control is not a department or organization chart group; it is a philosophy, a way of life for the effective business.

The classification of an expense as a variable does not imply that it will vary or change automatically with the level of operation. Timely cost control by management is important on variable expenses to cause or insure that these expenses vary with the operating levels.

In the early 1900's, virtually all costs were variable except for depreciation, insurance, and a few other expenses. In recent years, for practical purposes, more expenses are becoming fixed. Theoretically they are variable. In instances where productive labor employees can only be scheduled for three or four days per week and a five-day week must be maintained to prevent losing skilled employees, productive labor must be considered as fixed.

As business becomes more complex, employees available are generally more educated; and as automation steadily increases the investment in plant and equipment per employee, most industrial costs will become more fixed. Skilled, sophisticated, and effective management of resource allocation, production scheduling and inventory control will be required to maximize financial results. Managers may need to begin, now, to simulate virtually full fixed cost operation in order to be ready for these changes in the factors affecting decisions. Long run planning must replace short term reactions to insure the best performance.

SUMMARY

Manufacturing expenses are sometimes called conversion cost. Conversion costs are those costs required to convert materials into a product for subsequent processing or sale.

Variable expenses include operating supplies, fuel, electricity, water, and similar items. Fixed expenses include salaries, depreciation, and others. These costs should be based on engineered specifications and calculations.

Policies, instructions, and responsibilities should be prepared to define the reporting, calculation and control of operating supplies and repairs. Standards should be related to output production based on standard conditions. Averages and historical conditions should be avoided.

Replacement values are suggested for estimating depreciation to replace plant, property, and equipment in an inflated economy. However, for external financial reporting and tax accounting, acceptable accounting practices and government regulations must be followed. With accelerated depreciation methods and replacement values, it is difficult to use book depreciation based on original cost values for standard cost.

The cost per machine hour is recommended as the best basis to reflect the time or productivity of facilities. Other bases are analyzed.

The first objective of a standard costing and industrial planning system is to provide information for management decisions and control based on management objectives. Inventory pricing may be a secondary consideration.

In the years ahead, if the needs and desires of consumers change, businesses can expect to become more complex with more items and colors. More costs will become fixed rather than variable. Managers may need to begin to simulate virtually full fixed cost operation of more complex businesses in order to be ready for these changes and the factors affecting decisions. Planning must replace short term reaction to insure the best performance.

The data required for the calculation of standard manufacturing cost has been completed. The calculation of these standard manufacturing costs and their application to cost sheets will be covered in the next chapter.

CHAPTER SIX

Calculation of Manufacturing Costs

Manufacturing costs are those expenses which are required to produce a first quality product and make the product available at the point of manufacture for distribution to a warehouse or customer. Sometimes, the customer may be another division of the firm.

The basic manufacturing cost data compiled in the preceeding chapters shall now be converted to manufacturing cost for application to a cost sheet. Often, manufacturing costs are called conversion costs. These are the costs required for conversion or transformation of raw materials or partially fabricated parts into a finished or semi-finished product. These manufacturing expenses and other values are sometimes termed *value added* to the raw materials, or initial parts. The accepted total value formula is:

Value added = Net Market Value — (Materials + Supplies + Fuels)

Manufacturing or conversion costs include those associated with off-quality products, claims, returns, and other quality losses or mark-ups. Quality costs may be reduced, quality improved, and customers satisfied by the development of an effective quality program. Effective quality control may be a function that managers cannot afford *not* to incur. The emphasis of government agencies on consumer protection may be the result of inadequate quality control in some industries. Consumers are disillusioned by automobile recalls to correct defects, by appliances that require excess maintenance, and other product performance. Managers must insist that products are produced and guaranteed for a specified quality level. Cost reductions which reduce quality levels must be resisted.

Cost Sheet Design

The cost sheet for material costs as illustrated in Figure 3-12 can be expanded to include manufacturing costs as indicated in Figure 6-1. The cost centers shown are for the simulated firm developed in this text. These can be revised as may be required for most any industrial manufacturing operation. Only the productive cost centers are shown on the cost sheet. Service cost center expense has been distributed to these productive cost centers as shown in Figures 4-7, 4-9, and 5-7.

PRODUCT COST SHEET

PLANT ATLANTA		DIVISION HOME FURNISHINGS		SPEC. NO. 501		PRODUCT NO. 201		PRODUCT NAME ALL AMERICAN		CAL. NO. 6102	

CAL. BY + DATE		CHECKED BY		MATERIAL WT. 1,280 LB.		MACHINE 5/32 LOOP		SPI 7.0	SPEC. INSTR. NONE		

ITEM	LINE	ITEM	UNIT	SPEC. NO.	STD. UNITS	MAT. MULT.	ALWD. UNITS	STD. PRICE	COST PER UNIT (SQ. YD.) VARIABLE	FIXED	TOTAL
MATERIALS	1	YARN	LB	110	1.280	1.035	1.325	1.170	1.551	X.XXX	1.551
	2	OUTSIDE PROCESS	XX	XXX	X.XXX	X.XXX	X.XXX	X.XXX	X.XXX	X.XXX	X.XXX
	3	FIRST BACK	SY	224	1.000	1.020	1.020	0.200	0.204	X.XXX	0.204
	4	DYE + CHEMICALS	LB	980	1.850	1.075	1.990	0.028	0.056	X.XXX	0.056
	5	ADHESIVE	LB	214	1.625	1.050	1.710	0.080	0.137	X.XXX	0.137
	6	SECOND BACK	SY	225	1.000	1.020	1.020	0.160	0.163	X.XXX	0.163
	7	PACKAGE	SY	9210	1.000	1.025	1.025	0.030	0.031	X.XXX	0.031
	8	SUB-TOTAL: MATERIAL COST							2.142	X.XXX	2.142
MANUFACTURING	9	RECEIVE + TUFT		V	F		MH	UNITS			
	10	DYE	$8.22	V	$2.96 F	0.60 MH		100 UNITS	0.049	0.018	0.067
	11	DRY		V	F		MH	UNITS			
	12	ADHESIVE		V	F		MH	UNITS			
	13	OUTSIDE PROCESS		V	F		MH	UNITS			
	14	INSPECT + PACK		V	F		MH	UNITS			
	15	SHIP		V	F		MH	UNITS			
	16	SUB-TOTAL: MANUFACTURING COST - FIRST QUALITY									

FIGURE 6-1

COST SHEET WITH MANUFACTURING COSTS

Some industry cost sheets include costs through each center sub-totaled with materials being included as utilized at each cost center. This is primarily for inventory evaluation. The cost sheet in this example is designed to be easier for managers to understand. For firms with data processing installations, each line on the cost sheet can be numbered with data fields in the cards, tapes, or disc for each line and elemental data point. Programs may be written to sum by line number for each work-in-process inventory value.

The cost sheet shown in Figure 6-1 is primarily for the Cost Department and financial areas utilization. A simplified merchandising cost sheet will be developed for marketing and sales managers subsequently.

Calculation of Manufacturing Costs

For the dyeing costs of the simulated firm, the machine hour rates (from Figure 5-8) are:

Variable Labor =	$3.31 Per Machine Hour
Variable Manufacturing Expense =	$4.91 Per Machine Hour
Sub-Total: Variable Cost =	$8.22 Per Machine Hour
Fixed Manufacturing Expense =	$2.96 Per Machine Hour

From Figure 4-2, the machine hours per 100 square yards for Product Number 201 are 0.60 per 100 square yards. The variable and fixed costs shown on the cost sheet in Figure 6-1, line number 10, are:

Costs per Machine Hour	×	Machine Hours per 100 Square Yards	=	Cost per 100 Square Yards	÷ 100 =	Costs per Square Yard
$8.22 Variable	×	0.60	=	$4.93	÷ 100 =	$0.049
$2.96 Fixed	×	0.60	=	$1.78	÷ 100 =	$0.018
					Total =	$0.067

In most manufacturing operations, these costs would be marked up for subsequent material losses as illustrated in Figure 3-11, before arriving at the cost sheet values. Each process cost is the cost for a specific in-process manufacturing operation. The cost sheet reflects a packed unit ready for shipment, or transfer to another division. Therefore, in-process cost must normally be increased for losses from the particular process to packed production. In the case of the simulated plant which is being developed in this text, in-process losses are insignificant, except for materials. (The dyeing example is a batch process. Similar costing situations are found in many industrial operations.)

The machine hours for productive cost centers can be determined by the formula:

$$\frac{1.00}{\text{Net Output Production Units per Hour}} = \text{Machine Hours per Unit}$$

Units for various industries may be parts, pieces, gallons, pounds, square yards, linear yards, cubic feet or any related production characteristic. Machine hours are unit, per hundred units, or others may be utilized to obtain significant numbers without excessive decimal accuracy.

In the case of food processing industries for poultry—chickens, turkeys, and other products—the basis for cost may be per conveyor line hour, rather than an individual machine hour. As an example, assume a processing conveyor operates 50 feet per minute with birds on 6 inch centers. In this case, the production per conveyor hour is:

$$50 \text{ Feet per minute} \times 2 \text{ Birds per Foot} \times 60 \text{ Minutes per Hour} = \\ 6,000 \text{ Birds per Conveyor Line Hour}$$

With birds of a net weight of two pounds each, the pounds per hour would be:

$$6,000 \text{ Birds} \times 2.0 \text{ Pounds per Bird} = 12,000 \text{ Pounds per Conveyor Line Hour}$$

The conveyor line hours per 1,000 processed pounds, then, is:

$$\frac{1,000 \text{ Pounds}}{12,000 \text{ Pounds per Conveyor Line Hour}} = \frac{0.083 \text{ Conveyor Line}}{\text{Hours per 1,000 Pounds}}$$

Should birds of net weight of three pounds each be processed, the production would be 18,000 pounds per conveyor line hour or 0.055 conveyor line hours per 1,000 processed pounds. Knowing the cost per conveyor line hour, determined in the same manner that machine hour rates have been estimated, it is possible to calculate cost for various sizes of birds, conveyor speeds, and other dimensions.

In the case of conveyors and other production lines with high volume, it may be best to calculate rates on a per minute, rather than a per hour basis.

The food industry involving growing and processing live animals presents interesting problems of feed yields for various grow-out weights, processing weights, and optimum costing and pricing for various animal parts.

In most manufacturing operations involving parts or other units, a certain number of part "A's" can be produced for an equivalent number of part "B's". In the case of nuts and bolts, two washers (Part A) may be required for each nut (Part B)—and these can be scheduled and manufactured.

In the case of live poultry, once a bird has been hatched, grown, and processed, there are two legs, as an example, regardless of whether these fit into the market demand pattern. Linear programming may be an effective mathematical tool to aid managers in optimizing results with the various constraints of weights, parts, prices, market demand, and others.

For many industrial operations, machine hours, conveyor line hours, or similar rates provide the best basis for applying variable and fixed manufacturing expenses to product cost sheets. Percentages or multipliers of labor, materials, or other basis may be misleading. These may not adequately differentiate costs as related to production machine time by product.

Percentages tend to undercost low-priced products or products with a low labor content. Similarly, these percentages would over-cost higher priced products or those with a relatively higher labor content.

Managers must be careful to understand the basis for costs calculation of both variable and fixed cost for product mix evaluations. Sometimes, a specific product mix change may indicate better financial results. Then, equipment utilization analyses indicate that plant equipment utilization will be disrupted. Again, linear programming is a mathematical technique which can assist managers in optimizing these two parameters or other conditions—including raw material availability, warehouse requirements and others.

At this point, the calculation of the manufacturing costs of Product Number 201 for all other cost centers can be completed and inserted on the cost sheet as shown in Figure 6-2.

Receiving and Shipping Departments may not have an applicable machine hour basis. For receiving, it may be necessary to use pounds, cases, items, or some other

PRODUCT COST SHEET

PLANT ATLANTA		DIVISION HOME FURNISHINGS		SPEC. NO. 501		PRODUCT NO. 201		PRODUCT NAME ALL AMERICAN		CAL. NO. 6102

CAL. BY + DATE		CHECKED BY		MATERIAL WT. 1,280 LB.		MACHINE 5/32 LOOP	SPI 7.0	SPEC. INSTR. NONE		

ITEM	LINE	ITEM	UNIT	SPEC. NO.	STD. UNITS	MAT. MULT.	ALWD. UNITS	STD. PRICE	COST PER UNIT (SQ. YD.) VARIABLE	FIXED	TOTAL
	1	YARN	LB	110	1,280	1,035	1,325	1,170	1,551	X,XXX	1,551
	2	OUTSIDE PROCESS	XX	XXX	X,XXX	X,XXX	X,XXX	X,XXX	X,XXX	X,XXX	X,XXX
MATERIALS	3	FIRST BACK	SY	224	1,000	1,020	1,020	0,200	0,204	X,XXX	0,204
	4	DYE + CHEMICALS	LB	980	1,850	1,075	1,990	0,028	0,056	X,XXX	0,056
	5	ADHESIVE	LB	214	1,625	1,050	1,710	0,080	0,137	X,XXX	0,137
	6	SECOND BACK	SY	225	1,000	1,020	1,020	0,160	0,163	X,XXX	0,163
	7	PACKAGE	SY	9210	1,000	1,025	1,025	0,030	0,031	X,XXX	0,031
	8	SUB-TOTAL: MATERIAL COST							2,142	X,XXX	2,142
MANUFACTURING	9	RECEIVE + TUFT		$15.00 V	$10.00 F	0.45 MH	100 UNITS		0,068	0,045	0,113
	10	DYE		8.22 V	2.96 F	0.60 MH	100 UNITS		0,049	0,018	0,067
	11	DRY		27.00 V	11.00 F	0.07 MH	100 UNITS		0,019	0,008	0,027
	12	ADHESIVE		30.00 V	21.00 F	0.06 MH	100 UNITS		0,018	0,013	0,031
	13	OUTSIDE PROCESS		V	F	MH	UNITS		X,XXX	X,XXX	X,XXX
	14	INSPECT + PACK		25.00 V	20.00 F	0.06 MH	100 UNITS		0,015	0,012	0,027
	15	SHIP		1.96 V	2.38 F	0.75 MH	100 UNITS		0,015	0,018	0,033
	16	SUB-TOTAL: MANUFACTURING COST – FIRST QUALITY							2,326	0,114	2,440

FIGURE 6-2
MANUFACTURING COST—FIRST QUALITY

receiving unit. In some cases, combinations of standard may be necessary, particularly when receiving activities vary from rail cars to small item shipments.

As an example, a chemical receipt from a tank car which is pumped automatically may be a cost per 1,000 gallons. A truck load of parts may be on a costs per pallet. These bases which are a true measure of work content for control purposes must be related to other basis for application to cost sheets. In the case of the simulated firm, most receipts are pounds or rolls. These must be related to square yards for cost sheet application.

For a Shipping Department, the cost basis may be per roll, per case, or another basis rather than machine hours. In all cases, the basis should be on the "cause of costs" which generates the need for the service or work content. The standards per case, pallet, or other unit for Shipping or Receiving would be developed by Methods and Standards Engineers from studies of the man minutes of work content for each unit. These standards would be the basis for estimating crew size and overtime scheduling.

For the Shipping Department in the simulated firm, the following data are developed from Figures 4-7 and 5-7:

Expense	*Cost per Week*
Labor Costs:	
Productive Departments	$1,100
Service Departments	200
Variable Expense:	
Labor Expense	280
Manufacturing Expense	380
Sub-Total: Variable	$1,960
Fixed Expense:	
Manufacturing Expense	$2,382
Total	$4,342

Based on 1,000 rolls per week, the costs per roll are:

Variable Costs per Roll = $1,960 ÷ 1,000 Rolls = $1.96 per Roll
Fixed Cost per Roll   = $2,382 ÷ 1,000 Rolls = $2.38 per Roll

For cost sheet application to square yards, a roll (see Specification Sheet in Figure 2-9) contains 133 square yards.

The rolls per 100 square yards is:

$$\frac{100}{\text{Square Yards per Roll}} = \text{Rolls per 100 Square Yards}$$

$$\frac{100}{133} = 0.75 \text{ Rolls/100 Square Yards}$$

The cost sheet data, line number 15, are:

Expense	Costs per Roll		100 SY per Roll		Cost per 100 SY				Costs per Square Yard
Variable Cost	$1.96	×	0.75	=	$1.47	÷	100	=	$0.015
Fixed Cost	$2.38	×	0.75	=	$1.78	÷	100	=	$0.018

For this shipping example, rolls become the basis for costs calculation rather than machine hours. Other related bases would be selected for other industries. In the case of major appliances, such as washing machines, the costs basis could be per machine. For garments, it could be per case related to a costs per dozen. In the chemical industry, a cost per drum may be the basis which is transformed to a cost per 100 pounds or a cost per gallon for cost sheet application.

Defining Cost Centers

In some productive departments, machinery may be of similar classification; yet, certain machines may have different cost characteristics. This is true when certain machine tools have variations in precision or capability, machinery with unique controls, and other high cost features resulting in higher investment and depreciation.

As an example, machinery group "A" may have fixed manufacturing expenses of $4.00 per machine hour and group "B" $8.50 per machine hour. Should products be produced on these machines which require 0.10 machine hour per unit, the cost would be:

Machine Group	Fixed Cost per Machine Hour		Machine Hour per Unit		Cost per Unit
A	$4.00	×	0.10	=	$0.40
B	$8.50	×	0.10	=	$0.85

Often, a careful definition of cost centers can improve significantly the cost calculations and the determination of real costs for a product or an item.

Idle Capacity Costs

Management policy as shown in Figure 2-1, defines plant operations over the long run as two shifts, five days or 80 hours per week. This, then, results in one shift of idle capacity. For the long run, no costs are associated with this idle capacity for all variable and fixed costs are applied to the operating machine hours.

Yet, for this short run, idle capacity can exist for which there are related costs. Even though the long run operations may be 80 hours per week, year-to-year variations can be expected.

Assuming the sales forecast and machine hours are as shown in Figure 6-3 for the simulated firm, the question is, "How much 'idle capacity' real costs will result?" In this example, sixty hours per week will not be utilized from a standard cost point of view. The potential real costs losses, then, are:

Type Costs	*Costs per Machine Hour (Figure 5-8)*		*Idle Hours per Week*		*Loss per Week*	*Loss per Year*
Labor Costs:						
Productive Departments	$ 2.50	$\times$	60	=	$150	$ 7,500
Service Departments	0.81	$\times$	60	=	49	2,450
Variable Expenses:						
Labor Benefits	0.74	$\times$	60	=	44	2,200
Manufacturing Expenses	4.17	$\times$	60	=	250	12,500
Fixed Expenses:						
Manufacturing	2.96	$\times$	60	=	178	8,900
Total	$11.18				$671	$33,550

Dyeing Department

Product Number	Volume Units (100 SY) Per Year	Machine Hours Per 100 Units	Total Machine Hours Per Year	Machine Hours Per Week 50 Weeks/Year
101	40,000	0.40	16,000	320
201	20,000	0.60	12,000	240
301	10,000	0.80	8,000	160
401	4,000	1.00	4,000	80
601	4,000	1.25	5,000	100
Total Machine Hours Utilized =			45,000	+ 900
Total Machine Hours Available 12 Machines X 80 Hours Per Week =				- 960
Gain or (Loss) Machine Hours =				(- 60)

FIGURE 6-3

CALCULATION OF IDLE CAPACITY MACHINE HOURS

Effective production and employee scheduling could prevent the loss in the productive department labor and the related labor benefits. Variable manufacturing expenses which include fuel, electricity, and others should not be incurred. Most likely, the Service Department labor and benefits, along with fixed manufacturing expenses, would be a real loss.

A calculation for each cost center is necessary to balance the cost calculation and insure the accuracy of the conversion to cost sheet data. For the Dyeing Department, a worksheet is shown in Figure 6-4. In this case, a slight gain results as the cost sheet data is rounded to three decimal points.

Managers should insist that cost calculations and planning data are balanced to verify accuracy. In firms where thousands of products or stockkeeping units must be costed, a computer program to calculate and verify accuracy will be necessary. For planning and cost control systems for existing operations, these standard costs must be compared with actual costs to determine potential variances.

Dyeing Department

Product Number	Units Volume Per Year	Fixed Cost Per Unit	Total Fixed Cost Per Year
101	4,000,000	0.012	$ 48,000
201	2,000,000	0.018	36,000
301	1,000,000	0.024	24,000
401	400,000	0.029	11,600
501	Not Applicable	-	-
601	400,000	0.036	14,400
			$134,000
Fixed Manufacturing Expense Idle Capacity Loss			8,900
			$142,900
Fixed Manufacturing Expense, Figure 47			142,200
Gain or (Loss)			$ 700

FIGURE 6-4
FIXED MANUFACTURING COST VERIFICATION

By understanding cost calculations, managers can locate potential losses. This permits the effective manager to make decisions and take actions in advance to prevent these losses. In some cases, better production scheduling may be required. In other cases, a change in product mix may be necessary to improve and balance utilization of facilities.

In some cases, sales forecasts have been used for determining machine hours by department or cost center. Often, this results in a wide variation of machine hours within the plant. Department "A" may require 120 machine hours per week, Department "B" may need 100 machine hours per week, and Department "C" only 50 machine hours per week. In this case, there would not be any idle capacity from a standard costs standpoint. Yet, Department "B" and particularly Department "C" would have calculated a higher costs due to poor utilization of these departments.

When costs are being calculated for a new plant for which sales volume to fully utilize the facilities is not immediately available, the utilization of a sales forecast as a basis for machine hours can seriously distort total cost. This can be a burden to the sales effort for costs will appear abnormally high at the very time the competitive market pricing should be the most competitive in order to generate sales volume. In situations of this type, the contribution—net sales price minus the variable cost per unit—would be a valid basis for making decisions and evaluating market prices, rather than total cost calculations.

In non-standard cases of this type where sales expectations and production volumes vary widely, the utilization of variable cost may be the best basis for management analysis. Even variable cost can be distorted for small start-up operations where optimum operator assignments cannot be achieved.

For maximum effectiveness of new plants or operations, the long-run plant productivity and sales volume should be the basis for calculating manufacturing cost. The utilization of both variable cost and total cost gives managers two reference points, two guidelines from which to evaluate available market prices, rather than a single indicator of contribution or margin. Specific examples will illustrate these points in Chapter Nine relative to pricing.

In some situations, the price may be determined by what the customer is willing to pay for the product. Even in these cases, managers must know their real cost in order to evaluate market prices, and sort out those items, or customers who are not contributing significantly to financial results. The fact that prices may be more influenced by market conditions, rather than a particular firm's costs, does not reduce a manager's need for factual cost information for decisions and actions.

For managers to take action, it is best to determine the industry or long run expected normal operation and point up idle capacity cost as a reason for not attaining the desired financial results. *Managers must not permit costs to be hidden or confused by a method of calculation.*

Knowing real costs and the reasons for variations, managers can take actions today to be ready for the situation which will develop tomorrow. The difference between a superior manager and an average manager may be in the timing of decisions and actions. All management information on cost must be calculated and presented to enable managers to take action in advance. The best decisions are worthless after the money has been expended.

Costs of Quality

At this point, manufacturing costs have been calculated for a first quality manufactured product. The nature of production and manufacturing processes involving conversion and transformation of materials will create some off-quality units.

The quantity of off-quality products and grading standards employed vary from industry to industry and firm to firm depending on the objective criteria and precision of the products. Also, within a company, the quantity of off-quality production may vary from time to time depending on the emphasis managers may place on quality. This latter type of variation can be reduced by analytical and objective quality characteristic definitions and control. Quality control texts cover the detailed aspects of industrial quality control programs.

Many manufacturing plants have extensive quality reports on off-quality produced by type of defects and responsibility. Manufacturing managers tend to concentrate on these reports. In another part of the firm, possibly the Claims Department, a record should be maintained of claims from customers and the losses paid or allowed. These are for products which were graded first quality in manufacturing and, for various reasons, were not satisfactory to the customer.

Quality costs include graded off-quality in the plant plus losses on claims and returns, resulting from manufacturing faults. Claims and returns should be carefully analyzed to show the "cause of the complaint" and responsibility for the off-quality production. On some occasions, it may be a manufacturing defect which was missed by inspection. It is sometimes necessary to make a policy or customer relations settlement to keep customer goodwill, even when there is doubt about the validity of the claim. Losses due to handling, incorrect shipments, and arithmetic corrections may occur.

For the best financial results, managers must know the cause, responsibility, and costs of the total off-quality product regardless of whether it is classified in manufacturing, customer claim, or customer return of an off-quality fault.

Even with complete statistical data, the loss in goodwill and customer relations from off-quality is difficult to assess. A firm's image may well be one of a quality product or some variation in quality. In almost every industry, certain firms are known as leaders because of a superior quality product.

In the case of textiles, Greenwood Mills is noted for its trademark and its philosophy is discussed in its seventy-fifth anniversary book, *The Character of Quality*. Mr. J. C. Self, President of Greenwood Mills, in emphasizing the importance of quality relative to price stated, *"Business taken on price alone can be taken away between dinner and breakfast."* Managers of enterprises with reasonable prices and a superior quality product operate from a more secure position with less variation in volume and profits as year-to-year business conditions change.

Often, firms will develop product lines along a grade or quality basis. A superior quality product has one brand name, and an average quality product another brand. Automotive tires are an example of quality differentiation in products.

Given, then, that some off-quality is expected, how much does off-quality cost affect the costing of a specific product? The first quality manufacturing cost must be increased to recover expected quality losses. In Figure 6-5, a calculation of typical plant expected manufacturing off-quality mark-up is developed.

	Product "A"	Product "B"
Units Manufactured Per Year	1,200,000	500,000
Expected Off-Quality Units Per Year	45,000	30,000
Manufactured Costs - First Quality Per Unit	$2.44	$3.50
Total Manufacturing Costs - All Units	$2,928,000	$1,750,000
Target Net Selling Price for Off Quality Units	$1.14	$1.17
Loss Per Unit Off-Quality	$1.30	$2.33
Total Off-Quality Loss Per Year 45,000 X $1.30	$58,500	$69,900
Off-Quality Mark-up 58,500 ÷ $2,928,000	0.02	0.04

FIGURE 6-5

CALCULATION OF OFF-QUALITY MARK-UP

These should be developed by product or item or group of products or items where significant quality differences exist. Similar calculations can be made for claims and returns including non-manufacturing losses.

The quality costs for Product Number 201 have been included in the expanded cost sheet, Figure 6-6, line numbers 17, 18, and 19.

Manufacturing costs for a first quality unit must be increased from $2.440 to $2.508 or $0.068 per unit for expected losses resulting from off-quality products. This gives the manufacturing cost for an average quality unit.

It is important to notice from Figure 6-6 that the losses were reduced as a result

PRODUCT COST SHEET

PLANT		DIVISION	SPEC. NO.	PRODUCT NO.	PRODUCT NAME	CAL. NO.
ATLANTA		HOME FURNISHINGS	501	201	ALL AMERICAN	6102

CAL. BY + DATE   CHECKED BY   MATERIAL WT. 1,280 LB.   MACHINE 5/32 LOOP   SPI 7.0   SPEC. INSTR. NONE

ITEM	LINE	ITEM	UNIT	SPEC. NC.	STD. UNITS	MAT. MULT.	ALWD. UNITS	STD. PRICE	COST PER UNIT (SQ. YD.) VARIABLE	FIXED	TOTAL
MATERIALS	1	YARN	LB	110	1,280	1,035	1,325	1,170	1,551	X,XXX	1,551
	2	OUTSIDE PROCESS	XX	XXX	X,XXX	X,XXX	X,XXX	X,XXX	X,XXX	X,XXX	X,XXX
	3	FIRST BACK	SY	224	1,000	1,020	1,020	0,200	0,204	X,XXX	0,204
	4	DYE + CHEMICALS	LB	980	1,850	1,075	1,990	0,028	0,056	X,XXX	0,056
	5	ADHESIVE	LB	214	1,625	1,050	1,710	0,080	0,137	X,XXX	0,137
	6	SECOND BACK	SY	225	1,000	1,020	1,020	0,160	0,163	X,XXX	0,163
	7	PACKAGE	SY	9210	1,000	1,025	1,025	0,030	0,031	X,XXX	0,031
	8	SUB-TOTAL: MATERIAL COST							2,142	X,XXX	2,142
MANUFACTURING	9	RECEIVE + TUFT		$15.00 V	$10.00 F	0.45 MH	100 UNITS		0,068	0,045	0,113
	10	DYE		8.22 V	2.96 F	0.60 MH	100 UNITS		0,049	0,018	0,067
	11	DRY		27.00 V	11.00 F	0.07 MH	100 UNITS		0,019	0,008	0,027
	12	ADHESIVE		30.00 V	21.00 F	0.06 MH	100 UNITS		0,018	0,013	0,031
	13	OUTSIDE PROCESS		V	F	MH	UNITS		X,XXX	X,XXX	X,XXX
	14	INSPECT + PACK		25.00 V	20.00 F	0.06 MH	100 UNITS		0,015	0,012	0,027
	15	SHIP		1.96 V	2.38 F	0.75 MH	100 UNITS		0,015	0,018	0,033
	16	SUB-TOTAL: MANUFACTURING COST - FIRST QUALITY							2,326	0,114	2,440
QUALITY	17	PLANT OFF-QUALITY 0.0200 X LINE 16							0,047	0,002	0,049
	18	CLAIMS + RETURNS 0.0050 X LINE 16							0,012	0,001	0,013
	19	POLICY ADJUSTMENT 0.0025 X LINE 16							0,006	0,000	0,006
	20	SUB-TOTAL: MANUFACTURING COST - AVERAGE QUALITY							2,391	0,117	2,508

FIGURE 6-6

MANUFACTURING COST—AVERAGE QUALITY

of the sales or salvage value of off-quality units. For units which must be scrapped, losses may be relatively higher. Where data are available, loss calculations must be by product and by severity of the quality fault for the best calculation and control. Some specific defects may cause a greater, or lesser, off-quality loss than others.

Where processes permit reclaiming and potential reuse, a Reclaiming Department must be established as a cost center. In this case, detailed costs calculations, including yield losses, must be developed as with any other processing center.

The losses from off-quality products are generally the responsibility of manufacturing. The sale of off-quality products is a sales responsibility. Variances should be separated by quantity and price for analysis, and controlled by responsibility.

Policy and non-manufacturing adjustments are included in the quality section in order to handle all off-quality costs in one place for control purposes. In some cases, off-quality has been considered a failure to achieve selling prices, rather than a cost. In these cases, claims and returns have been shown as a mark-down in selling price. The separation of quality costs into several accounts increases quality control problems. The inclusion of policy or customer adjustments as a relationship to selling price sometimes misleads managers into believing that these are mandatory costs; such as terms, and cash discounts, rather than controllable costs. From a costing and practical standpoint, off-quality should be considered a cost, rather than a mark-down in selling prices.

Quality cost, regardless of the reasons, are real. These must be controlled and minimized in the same manner as any other expense.

Control of Quality Cost

In addition to the regular Quality Control Department reports of off-quality by product, defect, cause, and responsibility, managers require a report of losses by dollar value similar to Figure 6-7.

In this case, for plant off-quality, Product Number 201, even though plant off-quality units exceeded standard, a dollar gain resulted due to the higher than standard selling price for off-quality items. In this example, manufacturing managers are responsible for a loss variance of ($130) while sales is responsible for a gain of $246 in selling price (4,100 units × $0.06 per unit), or a net gain of $116. Where automated data processing equipment is available, detailed reports by product and type of defect can be obtained as may be required.

A report of this type requires adjustment to inventory to maintain a timely report. Off-quality may not be sold in the month produced. It is also essential for managers to follow up to insure that claims are being processed promptly and systematically. A memo entry of claims in process as indicated in Figure 6-7, may be a guide to potential losses.

Using the simulated example, manufacturing cost calculations have been completed for manufacturing to the delivery of first quality products to the plant warehouse. This is consistent with the firm's organizational chart as illustrated in Figure 2-2, and the manufacturing responsibilities as previously defined.

SUMMARY

Manufacturing costs are those expenses which are required to produce a first quality product and make products available at the point of manufacture for distribution to a warehouse or customer. These are sometimes termed conversion costs. These in-

PLANT: ATLANTA DATE: XX-XX-XX DIVISION: HOME FURNISHINGS RESPONSIBLE MANAGER:

ITEM	UNITS-OFF QUALITY STD.	ACTUAL	VARIANCE	SELLING PRICE PER UNIT STD.	ACTUAL	VARIANCE	TOTAL $ OFF QUALITY STD.	ACTUAL	VARIANCE	THREE MONTH $ OFF QUALITY STD.	ACTUAL	VARIANCE
PLANT QUALITY												
PRODUCT A												
PRODUCT 201	4,000	4,100	(100)	$1.14	$1.20	$0.06	$5,200	$5,084	$116	$16,500	$16,900	($400)
PRODUCT C												
CLAIMS + RETURNS												
PRODUCT A												
PRODUCT B												
PRODUCT C												
POLICY ADJUSTMENTS												
PRODUCT A												
PRODUCT B												
PRODUCT C												
MEMO ENTRY												
CLAIMS IN-PROCESS												
TOTAL												

FIGURE 6-7

SUMMARY OF OFF-QUALITY COSTS

clude those costs associated with off-quality products, claims, returns, and other quality losses.

Consumers are disillusioned at the recall of automobiles to correct defects, appliances which require excess service, and other product performance. Managers must insure that products are manufactured and guaranteed to a specified quality level.

For application to cost sheets, machine hours, machine minutes, or other time related basis is the best method of applying manufacturing cost to cost sheets. In the poultry processing industry, production per conveyor line hour may be the basis. These and other examples are illustrated. Percentages of labor, materials, and other bases of applying manufacturing costs are suspect.

The defining of cost centers and cost of idle capacity are discussed in this chapter. Verification of calculation accuracy is emphasized.

The cost control of off-quality products, claims, returns, and adjustments are an important area for improvement in cost calculation and control. These analyses must be by cause and responsibility for the best financial results. Quality cost must be differentiated by product, product group, or quality level.

The cost of quality should be considered an expense, rather than a markdown in sales prices. These must be controlled and minimized as any other expense.

The next phase of the firms operation is the effective and efficient distribution of these products to a satisfied customer. Securing optimum distribution cost is the subject of Chapter Seven.

CHAPTER SEVEN

Securing Efficient Distribution Costs

The distribution of a manufactured product from the point of manufacture to a customer may be the largest portion of cost for many firms. Distribution expense is the cost of servicing customer distribution needs.

The maintenance and control of an effective and efficient distribution of products to a satisfied customer is essential for the continued success of the firm. For many firms, controlled distribution to the ultimate consumer will be essential. Control does not imply ownership. It may be by exclusive products, confined territories, franchises, distribution agreements, financing or other influencing factors.

As indicated by the organization chart shown as Figure 2-2 in this example, the function of distribution services includes warehousing, order processing, production scheduling, sales service, traffic, shipping, claims service, and inventory control.

Channels of Distribution

The cost of distributing a product is influenced significantly by the channel of distribution or trade channel. The channels or routes which the product may take from the manufacturer to the customer are:

1. *Retail:* In this type, the firm has a sales force which contacts retail merchants, and accepts orders. Shipments and invoices are direct to the individual outlets. Sales orders may be relatively small and administrative costs are high due to the servicing of small orders and a large number of customers.
2. *Distributors:* For the firms which do not have direct retail sales, distributors may be the best method of distribution. A distributor purchases in large quantities from the manufacturer, maintains an inventory, and services retail outlets.
3. *National Accounts:* These are certain customers with large operations or major firms with multiple plants who purchase in large quantities.
4. *Private Label:* Large chain stores, mail order houses, and others selling consumer products may wish to market items under their own brand names, usually in large volumes.

5. *Direct:* In this case, the firm sells direct to the end-using customer. This includes most industrial products and certain selected consumer items; such as, brushes, small appliances, and other items handled door-to-door.
6. *Contract:* Firms which manufacture products to specific specifications of a customer or end use. Generally, contract distributed products have some unique features or quality levels as distinguished from the normal consumer or industrial market.
7. *International:* Sales outside the home market of a firm may be handled through one or more of the previous six channels. Special packaging cost, fixed expense application, and pricing is required.

From a costing standpoint, the key is the number of transactions or complexity. It is not the size of the initial order or contract which determines the cost. It is the number of production orders, shipments, invoices, or accounts receivable which *causes* costs.

A large contract for truck load shipments of complete units to a single point can result in lower costs. Yet, a large contract with shipments to multiple customers or stores will significantly change the cost and price required to generate a desired return on investment.

Should large contracts require the seller to warehouse inventories in multiple regional warehouses to provide customer service, the cost of distribution will increase substantially. An important factor is the inventory responsibility, particularly in consumer products involving many colors and products with a large number of stockkeeping items.

When products are made to order, rather than made to stock, the potential cost for carrying inventory and obsolescence will be reduced.

It is essential for managers to know the real cost by each channel of distribution in order to make analytical and objective decisions. Average cost conceals real cost and creates difficulties in profitability analysis. Sometimes, in cost calculations, retail sales have carried the fixed expenses of other channels of distribution.

In some industries, large volume contracts, national accounts, and private label orders have been considered extra business. Now, these channels of distribution are becoming such a large portion of demand that they must pay their own way. These channels must generate a reasonable return on investment. *Contribution to fixed cost is not enough.*

The only justifiable channel is one which performs the required functions efficiently. The distributor channel is very effective for manufacturers provided the services are efficiently performed—ordering in large quantities, maintenance of inventories, guaranteeing of inventory made to stock orders, and payment within normal credit terms. This trade channel fails when the distributors force these functions back onto the manufacturers.

In order to evaluate the efficiency of the alternative channels, simulation models may be developed to test how merchandise will flow through designated channels. The significant parameters of inventory, frequency of orders, size of orders, order filling time, modes of transportation, warehouse locations, and others must be included in the model. In the years ahead, managers will find it necessary to utilize models of distribution systems for analysis and decision. The determination of the best distribution system is too complex and important to be left to judgment or trial and error methods.

In this chapter, distribution cost will be evaluated, and methods of separating these costs by channel of distribution will be developed.

Fixed Distribution Staff

For the simulated firm, the salary budgets for the Distribution Services Staff is shown in Figure 7-1.

It is important to consider that the simulated firm is a mass market producer. Business with unusual style, unusual design, and low volume per invoice or shipment would require a larger staff per dollar of sales. The key to low distribution cost is simplicity. A broad product line and small invoices will create complexity and high distribution cost.

Whether an order is for $50 or $10,000, an order must be written, credit checked, order acknowledged, shipment and bill of lading prepared, invoiced, entered into accounts receivable, inventory transaction recorded, and sales statistics accumulated. This work causes transaction cost in Distribution and Administration. In the case of items where the manufacturer pays freight, the additional freight cost for minimum charge shipments added to transaction cost can eliminate profit potential on small orders. Where managers are confronted with this situation, price breaks and volume discounts are effective.

The simulated firm concentrates, too, on the large volume market areas. It does not attempt to dilute its resources by covering all geographical areas in the home market.

Warehouse Location

The simulated firm in this example has five warehouses which are in Los Angeles, Dallas, Chicago, New York, and Atlanta as indicated on the map in Figure 7-2. Atlanta is the home office and manufacturing point. The determination of the optimum number of warehouses and their geographical location is beyond the scope of this text. However, these factors can be evaluated given freight, volume, inventory, and other cost considerations.

Sometimes, the firm's policy of customer service may override cost considerations in determining the number and location of regional warehouses. The difficulty in warehousing studies is placing a value on improved delivery to customers. Often, a warehouse must be located simply to meet competitive conditions in an important market area.

Given that a warehouse is required, the next consideration is to determine whether the firm should own and operate the warehouse or use a public warehouse. Volume, service, and cost factors will enable the managers to select a good alternative. In this example, public owned or contract operated warehouses are utilized.

Job Title	Staff	Salary	Travel Expense	Expected Bonus	Total	Charge to Retail Accounts	Charge to Large Volume Accounts
Director of Distribution Services	1	$25,000	$2,500	$2,500	$30,000	$24,000	$6,000
Executive Secretary	1	6,000	0	0	6,000	4,800	1,200
Production Control Mgr.	1	12,000	0	1,000	13,000	10,400	2,600
Production Controllers	3	24,000	0	0	24,000	16,000	8,000
Sales Service Mgr.	1	12,000	500	1,000	13,500	12,150	1,350
Sales Service Controllers	5	40,000	0	0	40,000	32,000	8,000
Order Entry Clerks	3	18,000	0	0	18,000	16,200	1,800
Inventory Clerks	3	18,000	0	0	18,000	16,200	1,800
Claims Service Mgr.	1	12,000	500	1,000	13,500	12,150	1,350
Secretary/Clerk	1	5,000	0	0	5,000	4,500	500
Traffic Manager	1	12,000	500	1,000	13,500	12,150	1,350
Secretary/Clerk	1	5,000	0	0	5,000	4,500	500
Totals		$189,000	$4,000	$6,500	$199,500	$165,050	$34,450

FIGURE 7-1

DISTRIBUTION SERVICES SALARY BUDGET

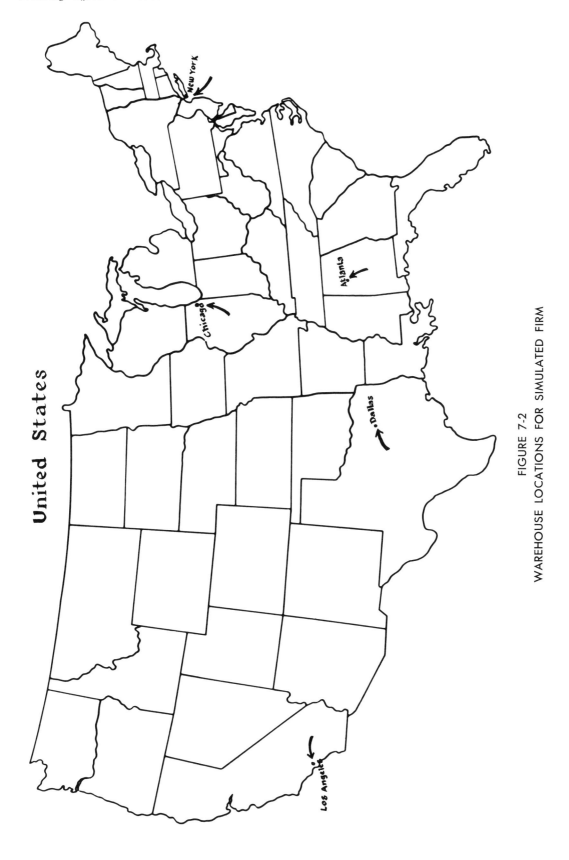

FIGURE 7-2
WAREHOUSE LOCATIONS FOR SIMULATED FIRM

Warehouse Cost

For the text example, the normal shipping volume is 1,000 rolls per week shipped from the manufacturing point. Of these, 200 rolls are shipped FOB manufacturing point to national accounts, private label, distributors or other large volume customers. Of the remaining 800 rolls, 400 rolls are shipped FOB manufacturing point to other customers and 400 rolls are shipped via warehouses to other customers.

The warehouse cost, then, is:

		Week	*Year*
In and out charge @ $2.00/Roll		$ 800	$40,000
Storage—$1.04/Month/Roll		600	30,000
Inventory of 2,400 Rolls			
	Total	$1,400	$70,000

The minimum guarantee per year for each warehouse outside of Atlanta is $8,000 or $32,000 per year for four warehouses. This portion of the cost will be considered as fixed expense. The net result for the simulated firm would be a variable and fixed expense summary:

	Week	*Year*
Variable Warehouse Cost	$ 760	$38,000
Fixed Warehouse Cost	640	32,000
Total Warehouse Cost	$1,400	$70,000

Should a firm operate warehouses, it is necessary to go through the calculation of cost similar to manufacturing cost calculation. These must include depreciation, labor, electricity, and all other expenses.

Transportation Cost

The cost of transporting products from the point of manufacture to warehouses or customers must be determined and controlled in the same manner as other expenses. Sometimes, firms either do not know or conceal certain expenses of freight movement, particularly where company owned trucks are utilized.

An example of an operating cost estimate for a tractor and trailer is shown in Figure 7-3. This particular example is for a long haul route from the southeast to California involving forty-five round trips annually each year. A 300 h.p., double axle tractor is required due to mountainous terrain in route. The trailer is non-refrigerated. At 27,000 pounds per load, a total of 1,215,000 pounds is hauled annually. On two-thirds of the trips, a return load is available which recovers $20,000 per year.

This example involves a very high utilization of equipment, with a cost of $0.36 per mile. With lower utilization, the cost per mile could reach $0.45 or more. For single axle tractors, lower cost would accrue. The estimate of truck cost is influenced by many factors. In the desert areas, recapped tires may not be feasible. Consequently, a higher

	Cost Per Tractor	Cost Per Trailer	Total Cost Per Rig
Fixed Cost:			
Depreciation - 4 yrs.	$5,000	$1,000	
Taxes & License	1,200	300	
Fire & Theft Insurance	250	50	
PL/PD Insurance	1,400	300	
Collision Insurance	1,000	200	
Garage & Parking	250	50	
Administrative Expense	500	100	
Sub-Total: Fixed Costs	$9,600	$2,000	$11,600
Variable Cost:			
Diesel Fuel	9,500	-	
Oil, Grease, & Anti-freeze	2,000	500	
Tires, Tubes, & Repairs	3,600	2,900	
Repairs & Maintenance	8,500	1,600	
Drivers, Benefits, & Expense	30,500	-	
Standby Rental	2,500	500	
Sub-Total: Variable Costs	$56,600	$5,500	$62,100
Total Cost Per Year	$66,200	$7,500	$73,700
Miles Per Year			205,000
Cost Per Mile			$0.36

FIGURE 7-3
ESTIMATE TRUCK OPERATING COSTS

cost would result for trucks operating over these areas. In other situations, insurance rates may be higher. With trucking service requiring a high utilization of equipment, standby rental must be included to maintain effective service.

Most truck costs are calculated per mile. This is a good basis for long hauls. However, for local, city deliveries with traffic delays, a cost per truck hour or cost per delivery may be a better basis to sort out the cost of small deliveries. Cost and budgets should be separated by major type of equipment, over-the-road, and local or inter-company hauling.

The question of leasing versus private ownership affects cost and return on investment. Other texts and publications cover the analysis and tax implications of this financial decision. Managers must insure that all cost analysis involving private ownership are complete and include all costs elements.

Comparing alternative methods, Figure 7-4, the least cost method of moving freight in this example would be via rail piggyback. Yet, managers must consider other factors including service and inventory. Transportation time affects inventory in the pipe line. Products having a high value or likely susceptibility to damage may incur in transit cost which offset other operating gains.

Pounds Moved Per Year	1,215,000

Private Truck - Figure 60

Cost of Private Truck	$73,700
Less Return Haul Revenue	20,000
Net Cost Per Year	$53,700

Rail Piggyback

Piggyback Rate	3.50 CWT
Piggyback Cost Per Year	$42,525

Common Carrier

Common Carrier Rate	$ 4.10 CWT
Common Carrier Cost Per Year	$49,815

FIGURE 7-4
EVALUATION OF ALTERNATIVE FREIGHT COST

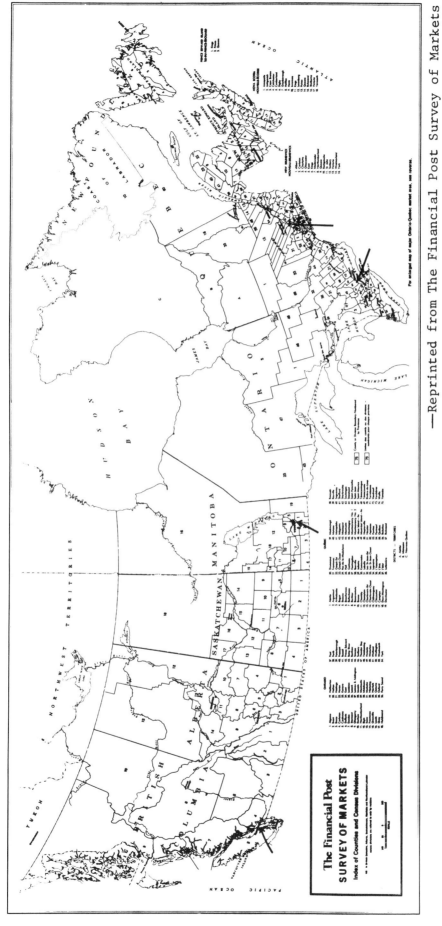

—Reprinted from The Financial Post Survey of Markets

FIGURE 7-5

CANADIAN WAREHOUSE LOCATIONS

Managers must constantly monitor truck operations to insure efficient utilization and control. Only products which are really required at other points should be moved. Transportation supervisors must resist the urge to fill up a trailer just to lower the cost per unit for freight movement.

For the simulated firm, transportation is considered to be via rail piggyback to the west coast and common carrier to other points. The freight costs are:

West Coast:	3 Piggyback trucks/week (45 weeks/year)	$127,575
Other points		167,425
Total:	Variable Freight Cost	$295,000

When a firm's products require small shipments, the freight cost can be a very significant portion of total sales dollars. As an example, visualize a Canadian manufacturer of items shipped prepaid in cases of 100 pounds each. The plant is located in Montreal. There are three warehouses located in Toronto, Winnipeg, and Vancouver (see Figure 7-5). A shipment to any area may go by four alternatives:

(a) Truck loads (TL) to warehouses; then, minimum charge to the customer.
(b) Truck loads to warehouses; then, less than truck load (LTL) to the customer.
(c) Minimum charge rate direct from Montreal to the customer.
(d) Less than truck load rate direct from Montreal to the customer.

Shipments are prepaid. Typical freight rates in Canadian dollars to two points from the Montreal manufacturing point are shown in Figure 7-6.

With these data, the cost for one, two and three case shipments are:

	Toronto Area			Vancouver Area		
	One Case	Two Cases	Three Cases	One Case	Two Cases	Three Cases
Freight to Warehouse (TL)	$2.00	$4.00	$ 6.00	$ 4.00	$ 8.00	$12.00
Warehouse to Customer	5.00	5.00	6.75	6.50	6.50	9.00
Total	$7.00	$9.00	$12.75	$10.50	$14.50	$21.00
Cost per Case	$7.00	$4.50	$ 4.25	$10.50	$ 7.25	$ 7.00

In a situation of this type, careful attention must be given to forecasting expected shipments by geographical area, route, and size of shipment. Computer programs may be required to estimate expected freight cost accurately, including freight rate changes.

With small shipments, it is important that price breaks be developed to minimize freight cost. In the earlier example, the freight cost alone justifies a substantial price difference between one and three case shipments. The determination of price breaks will be discussed in more detail in Chapter Nine.

In some cases, manufacturers have adopted pricing by geographical zone to re-

	Montreal to Toronto	Montreal to Vancouver
Truck Load (TL)	$2.00 CWT	$4.00 CWT
Less than Truck Load (LTL)	2.50 CWT	5.00 CWT
Minimum Charge (Less than 250 Pounds)	5.00	12.00

	Toronto Warehouse to Customer	Vancouver Warehouse to Customer
LTL	$2.25 CWT	$3.00 CWT
Minimum Charge (Less than 200 Pounds)	5.00	6.50

FIGURE 7-6

FREIGHT RATES IN CANADIAN DOLLARS

cover the added freight cost to more distant points. This may be effective when competition does not have manufacturing points in the more distant zones. In the U.S. market, zone pricing may be declining as more and more industries locate plants in important geographical areas, or equalize freight expense to the customer. Zone pricing and equalized freight charges are more feasible in industries with few suppliers. In most consumer products, multiple suppliers reduce the possibility of zone pricing, or freight equalization.

For major industries, such as automobiles, in which there are a relatively few suppliers, the freight cost may be equated to all geographical areas. In some industries, a $1.00 CWT may be allowed to all customers regardless of destination or real costs. Most likely, industry practice will dictate the specific approach to be utilized in shipping and billing freight to customers.

Last year's average freight cost per pound, per case, or per dollar of sales may not accurately represent next year's costs. When new products are added, locations of warehouses changed, or product mix altered, substantial year to year distortions can result in real freight cost.

Where multiple warehouses are utilized, a computerized system of forecasting and inventory control may be necessary to insure that the minimum quantity of inventory is maintained consistent with customer service requirements. Inventory optimization may justify inter-warehouse movements. Managers must insure that specific responsibility is assigned and control techniques are developed to prevent a build-up of excess inventory and costs in a multiple regional warehouse distribution system. Control is essential to insure that minimum inventories are maintained of low volume, discontinued, or obsolete items.

Basically, distribution cost is related to volume for a geographical area. As an example, Canada is geographically larger than the United States. A substantial part of the total retail trade is in four metropolitan centers. Yet, the Canadian population and resulting demand is about one-tenth that of the U. S. market. This results in a substantial higher cost for distribution of similar products in Canada as related to the United States.

Distribution Services Expense

For the simulated firm, the total cost of Distribution Services is shown in Figure 7-7.

Organizationally, Distribution Services is responsible for inventory control. Consequently, inventory related costs of insurance, taxes, and others are considered to be a distribution responsibility.

The variable cost for large volume customers—contract, distributors, national accounts, and private label—is relatively small, primarily, because all shipments for these channels of distribution are FOB the manufacturing point, and involve few invoices with large dollar values.

The separation of fixed expense by product line is based on the *cause* of each cost item. This may require the definition of the account to be based on this concept rather than using definitions which may be existing in the firm's chart of accounts.

The salaries and salary-related expenses of social security, hospital and group insurance, employee education and training, and others, were separated based on individual job duties or work content. Once salaries are properly separated by channel of distribution, all other salary related expenses can be calculated directly. An example of this type calculation was shown in Figure 4-5.

In the case of taxes and insurance on property, this can be estimated based on the building and equipment utilized. For inventory costs of insurance and taxes, most statistical forecasting and production planning systems have provisions to calculate expected inventory based on sales volume, service level, and lead time. Using these data, standard inventory taxes and insurance can be estimated by item. Therefore, these may be separated by channel of distribution.

Telephone and telegraph charges for long distance can be separated based on actual usage. In the case where no prior experience is available, the expected transactions may be a basis.

In certain distribution costs, including data processing and postage, the cause of a cost may be the complexity or number of transactions handled. The rapid increase in postal rates may require managers to develop alternate methods of transmitting information. Revisions of systems may be necessary, particularly in acknowledging orders, to reduce administrative and postage costs.

The effect of transactions will be more evident in administrative expense. Entering an order, acknowledging an order, posting records are the cause of transaction costs.

	Large Volume Customers ($000)	Retail Customers ($000)	Total ($000)	Basis
Variable Cost				
Freight to Warehouse	$ -	$295	$295	Direct
Warehouse Expense	-	38	38	Direct
Power & Fuel	2	3	5	Bldg. & Equip. Utilized
Sub-Total:	$ 2	$336	$338	
Fixed Cost				
Warehouse Expense	$ -	$ 32	$ 32	Direct
Salaries & Bonus	33	162	195	Direct
Travel Expense	1	3	4	Direct
Taxes - Property	1	4	5	Bldg. & Equip. Utilized
Taxes - Inventory	10	80	90	Inventory Val.
Insurance - Inventory	1	5	6	Inventory Val.
Insurance - Property	-	1	1	Bldg. & Equip. Utilized
Depreciation	3	12	15	Direct
Salary Continuation & Pension	2	7	9	Direct
Social Security	2	7	9	Direct
Hospital & Group Insurance	2	7	9	Direct
Employee Education & Training	2	6	8	Direct
Unemployment Compensation	-	2	2	Direct
Data Processing Rent & Supplies	5	35	40	Transaction
Dues & Subscriptions	-	1	1	Direct
Postage	1	9	10	Transaction
Telephone & Telegraph - Area	2	18	20	Direct
Telephone & Telegraph - Long Distance	1	6	7	Direct
Office Supplies	1	4	5	Transaction
Sub-Total:	$67	$401	$468	
Total:	$69	$737	$806	

FIGURE 7-7

DISTRIBUTION SERVICES EXPENSE PER YEAR

A transaction for an order for $5,000 can cause the same amount of work in these areas as a $500 order. Input data for a customer must be created; a card, tape, or disc record created and processed in Data Processing for each order. Therefore, it is important for managers to determine and know the real *cost of complexity* to properly evaluate the contribution of profitability of certain channels of distribution.

There may come a time, as business with low average order size grows, that existing systems will break down. It may simply not be possible to achieve certain higher sales volume due to the inability to handle paper. It is in this environment that real time, online computer systems must be considered.

Sometimes there is a feeling that certain expenses cannot be separated or assigned to specific product lines or channels of distribution. Yet, in almost every case when a detailed, industrial engineering work measurement type of approach is utilized, a cause or reason for the expense can be determined. In addition, these type studies point-up areas for potential cost reduction and improved control.

Managers must insist that all costs are defined and controlled. The urge to summarize accounts, particularly fixed expenses, must be avoided to achieve an effective and efficient distribution system.

Given these costs data, the distribution expenses may be summarized as indicated in Figure 7-8 for the normal operation of fifty weeks per year.

	Variable Expense	Fixed Transactions Expense	Fixed Other Expense	Total Cost
Retail Product Line	$6,720	$ 960	$7,060	$14,740
Rolls Per Week	800	800	800	800
Costs Per Roll	$ 8.40	$1.20	$ 8.83	$ 18.43
Large Volume Product Line	$ 40	$ 140	$1,200	$ 1,380
Rolls Per Week	200	200	200	200
Costs Per Roll	$ 0.20	$0.70	$ 6.00	$ 6.90

FIGURE 7-8
SUMMARY OF DISTRIBUTION EXPENSE

Calculation of Distribution Cost

With these budgets and data per roll for the text example, the cost per unit for application to the cost sheet can be determined. As an example, the retail customers' costs of $336,000 per year is $6,720 per week based on fifty weeks as normal operation. This, then, is $8.40 per roll or unit shipped.

The units per shipment can be obtained from the Specification Sheet (Figure 2-9). For the Product Number 201 which is being calculated, 133 square yards per roll are being shipped. For other industries, the unit could be gallons, pounds, dozens, or other applicable bases.

The costs for Product Number 201, shown in Figure 7-9, line number 22, are determined by:

	Large Volume		Retail	
	Variable	Fixed	Variable	Fixed
Cost per Roll	$0.20	$6.70	$8.40	$10.03
Units per Roll	133	133	133	133
Costs per Roll	$0.002	$0.050	$0.063	$0.075

The costs of distribution are substantially higher for the retail channel of distribution as a result of the costs of transportation and outside regional warehouses. In this case, shipments to retail customers FOB the manufacturing point and through warehouses are merged. In many cases, these different types of shipments must be separated for costing and control purposes.

The truly significant area requiring managers attention in the years ahead will be developing and controlling the distribution system and resulting costs. The question may be, "Is the objective to be manufacturer or marketer?" In the past decade, firms have often concentrated on obtaining control of vertical manufacturing operations and sources of material supplies. The next decade will require this emphasis to shift to control of distribution, markets, and customers. As an example, a chemical manufacturer may supply in-plant equipment for dispensing chemicals to customers who will purchase certain chemical supplies. This is a way to obtain some customer control and continuity of sales and to make it more difficult for competitors to compete with these particular customers.

SUMMARY

The maintenance and control of an effective and efficient distribution system is essential for the continued success of a business.

Certain orders or sales create complexity; and thereby, cause cost rather than contribute to profit. Managers must know the real cost by channel of distribution to make effective analysis of markets, customers, or trade channels. Average cost conceals real cost and creates difficulties in profitability analysis.

The number and location of warehouses, leased versus private ownership of trucks, and estimation of transportation cost by alternate methods are covered in this chapter. An example of the cost for distribution in Canada is included.

Distribution expenses are those costs incurred to make a product or item available from point of manufacture through delivery to a satisfied customer. These include transportation, warehouse charges, inventory cost, and other items.

The cost sheet has been expanded in Figure 7-9 to include selling, marketing, research and development, and administrative expenses. These costs and their control are the topic of Chapter 8, "Estimating Fixed Expenses and Investments."

PRODUCT COST SHEET

PLANT ATLANTA		DIVISION HOME FURNISHINGS	SPEC. NO. 501	PRODUCT NO. 201	PRODUCT NAME ALL AMERICAN	CAL. NO. 6102

CAL. BY + DATE   CHECKED BY   MATERIAL WT.   MACHINE   SPI   SPEC. INSTR.
                                            1,280 LB.   5/32 LOOP   7.0   NONE

ITEM	LINE	ITEM	UNIT	SPEC. NO.	STD. UNITS	MAT. MULT.	ALWD. UNITS	STD. PRICE	COST PER UNIT (SQ. YD.)		
									VARIABLE	FIXED	TOTAL
M A T E R I A L S	1	YARN	LB	110	1,280	1,035	1,325	1,170	1,551	X,XXX	1,551
	2	OUTSIDE PROCESS	XX	XXX	X,XXX	X,XXX	X,XXX	X,XXX	X,XXX	X,XXX	X,XXX
	3	FIRST BACK	SY	224	1,000	1,020	1,020	0,200	0,204	X,XXX	0,204
	4	DYE + CHEMICALS	LB	980	1,850	1,075	1,990	0,028	0,056	X,XXX	0,056
	5	ADHESIVE	LB	214	1,625	1,050	1,710	0,080	0,137	X,XXX	0,137
	6	SECOND BACK	SY	225	1,000	1,020	1,020	0,160	0,163	X,XXX	0,163
	7	PACKAGE	SY	9210	1,000	1,025	1,025	0,030	0,031	X,XXX	0,031
	8	SUB-TOTAL: MATERIAL COST							2,142	X,XXX	2,142
M A N U F A C T U R I N G	9	RECEIVE + TUFT		$15.00 V	$10.00 F	0,45 MH	100 UNITS		0,068	0,045	0,113
	10	DYE		8,22 V	2,96 F	0,60 MH	100 UNITS		0,049	0,018	0,067
	11	DRY		27,00 V	11,00 F	0,07 MH	100 UNITS		0,019	0,008	0,027
	12	ADHESIVE		30,00 V	21,00 F	0,06 MH	100 UNITS		0,018	0,013	0,031
	13	OUTSIDE PROCESS		V	F	MH	UNITS		X,XXX	X,XXX	X,XXX
	14	INSPECT + PACK		25,00 V	20,00 F	0,06 MH	100 UNITS		0,015	0,012	0,027
	15	SHIP		1,96 V	2,38 F	0,75 MH	100 UNITS		0,015	0,018	0,033
	16	SUB-TOTAL: MANUFACTURING COST - FIRST QUALITY							2,326	0,114	2,440
Q U A L I T Y	17	PLANT OFF-QUALITY 0.0200 X LINE 16							0,047	0,002	0,049
	18	CLAIMS + RETURNS 0.0050 X LINE 16							0,012	0,001	0,013
	19	POLICY ADJUSTMENT 0.0025 X LINE 16							0,006	0,000	0,006
	20	SUB-TOTAL: MANUFACTURING COST - AVERAGE QUALITY							2,391	0,117	2,508

ITEM	LINE	DISTRIBUTION, SELLING, RESEARCH AND ADMINISTRATIVE EXPENSES	LARGE VOLUME		RETAIL	
			VARIABLE	TOTAL	VARIABLE	TOTAL
	21	SUB-TOTAL: MANUFACTURING COST - AVERAGE QUALITY	2,391	2,508	2,391	2,508
S E L L I N G	22	DISTRIBUTION SERVICES	0,002	0,052	0,063	0,138
+ O T H E R	23	SELLING + MARKETING				
	24	RESEARCH + DEVELOPMENT				
	25	ADMINISTRATION				
	26	TOTAL: COST + NET BREAKEVEN PRICE				

FIGURE 7-9
DISTRIBUTION SERVICES COST CALCULATION

CHAPTER EIGHT

Estimating Fixed Expenses
and Investments

The determination of selling, marketing, research, development, and administrative expenses by channel of distribution is an essential element of an effective business plan. In some industries—tobacco, detergents, and others—these non-manufacturing expenses are the most important part of a planning and control system.

The first step is to determine a budget or what these expenses *should be* rather than use last year's historical average expense. The chart of accounts must be constructed to insure that each account is properly defined to provide data for separation of expenses based on the *cause* of the expense. These divisions should relate to individual responsibilities for the person in the firm who can take action to control the particular expenses.

Budget Specification Sheet

A Budget Specification Sheet should be prepared for each account as indicated in Figure 8-1. This example utilizes variable budgeting of expenses based on the actual payment schedule. Sometimes, a fixed amount is charged for each accounting period to even out large expenses over the fiscal year, regardless of when actual payment of the account may occur. Variable or *time-phased* budgeting with payments budgeted in the amount by time period of payment is necessary for proper control. It is essential for the preparation of actual cash requirements, by accounting period, or source and application of funds estimates.

This example is for a quarterly time interval. A monthly or four-week budget period is more effective for timely control and management decisions. The Budget Specification Sheet should be supported by a detailed worksheet listing each association or expense and the related costs for management consideration.

143

BUDGET SPECIFICATION SHEET	Account No. : 7012
	Account Name: Association Fees

Description of Account:

All fees paid to trade or industry associations, such as American Management Association, National Industrial Conference Board, American Marketing Association, and other similar groups.

Budget	Last Year Actual	Quarterly Budget				Next Year Budget
		3/31	6/30	9/30	12/31	
Administration	$10,400	$10,000	$2,000	-	-	$12,000
Marketing	1,600	1,600	-	$2,500	-	4,100
Sales	4,000	-	1,900	5,000	-	6,900
Research & Development	2,000	1,000	400	600	-	2,000
Total	$18,000	$12,600	$4,300	$8,100	-	$25,000

Reasons for Changes in Budget:

1. Marketing & Sales joined additional associations for certain executives and salesmen.

Issued By:	Approved by:	Responsibility:	Budget XXXX

FIGURE 8-1
BUDGET SPECIFICATION SHEET

Budget Control

For expense control, a budget control statement similar to Figure 8-2 is helpful. Most financial statements include comparisons of budgets to actual expenses, by division or departmental responsibility. In many firms, certain persons with budget control responsibility do not receive complete financial statements. In these cases, a supplementary or summary statement of this type is necessary.

ACCOUNT NAME: ASSOCIATION FEES   QUARTER ENDING: 6-30

ACCOUNT NUMBER: 7012   RESPONSIBILITY: VICE-PRESIDENT

DESCRIPTION OF ACCOUNT:

    ALL FEES PAID TO TRADE OR INDUSTRY ASSOCIATIONS, SUCH AS

    AMERICAN MANAGEMENT ASSOCIATION, NATIONAL INDUSTRIAL

    CONFERENCE BOARD, AMERICAN MARKETING ASSOCIATION, AND

    OTHER SIMILAR GROUPS.

BUDGET: SEE BUDGET SPECIFICATION SHEET AND DETAIL WORKSHEETS.

COST COMPARISON

QUARTER ENDING	BUDGET	ACTUAL	VARIANCE	YEAR TO DATE
3-31	$12,600	$12,100	$ 500	$ 500
6-30	4,300	4,400	(100)	400
9-30	8,100			
12-31	0			
TOTAL	$25,000			

EXPLANATION OF VARIANCE:

  1. $500 GAIN QUARTER ENDING 3-31 RESULTED FROM THE REDUCTION OF

    MEMBERSHIP FEES IN ONE ASSOCIATION.

FIGURE 8-2

BUDGET CONTROL STATEMENT

Summary of Expenses

Once individual budgets are completed, these may be summarized as shown in Figure 8-3. In most cases, these expenses can be assigned directly to responsible departments. As an example, consider Association Fees, Figure 8-1, $11,000 is directly assignable to Sales and Marketing. Salaries and bonuses, travel expenses, and other similar expenses may be assigned directly from these budgets. Data Processing expenses can, for example, be related to computer hours.

In situations where accounts are properly defined and budgeted, there is little need for allocation in order to accomplish distribution to departments.

In large organizations, a substantial portion of administrative expense is accumulated at the corporate headquarters. This may be assigned to the division on the basis of a formula in a lump sum. This leads to misunderstanding and difficulties at the divisional level in cost determination. All expenses from corporate or other similar locations should be separated to divisions by cause, and by account. Frequently, these expenses are related to complexity of the division's business, rather than sales, investment, or other general statistics. In some firms, these statistics have been used for formulating the division's share of corporate expense. This is a simple and easy way; however, management must insist that the correct and right method—cause of costs, transactions, or computer utilization—be the basis.

Centralized management information centers built around large computer systems can result in large corporate office expenses. These expenses must be charged to divisions on a utilization basis, not a percent of sales or other simple, easy, or arbitrary basis.

The expense of company-owned or leased aircraft is becoming a significant item. In firms where aircraft are owned, the expenses should be summarized and accounted for in a manner similar to that illustrated for trucking expense. Aircraft expenses should be separated between fixed and variable items, with a resulting cost calculation per hour of flying time by type of aircraft. Strict control is required to insure that the company owned planes are being used effectively and contributing to improved performance of the firm. Budgets must be developed and expenses charged to the department or person responsible for aircraft usage.

Rather than purchase a company airplane, some firms prefer to lease these services from a firm operating a fleet of airplanes. In this case, a minimum number of flying hours may be purchased annually with an agreement for the cost per hour for all excess hours. This type of service offers the firm a variety of aircraft with the selection depending on particular flight requirements. The guaranteed portion of the annual contract is fixed expense; whereas, the excess cost may be considered variable.

R & D Expense

Research and Development expenses vary extensively between firms depending on the industry and technology requirements. It is important that all expenses related to R & D be charged into this department's responsibility account. Important items are often materials and supplies used in development projects. In addition to these, manufacturing machinery, labor, or expenses which are utilized by the R & D department in the production of samples or prototype product should be charged to this department's account.

Research and Development effort should establish a budget for expenditures con-

SUMMARY OF SALES, RESEARCH, ADMINISTRATION
AND DISTRIBUTION FIXED EXPENSE
(000)

Account	Sales/Marketing	R & D	Division Administration	Corporate Administration	Total	Basis For Distribution
Salaries & Bonus	$ 712	$106	$ 330	$ 83	$1,231	Direct
Travel Expense- Auto & Commercial	144	7	17	2	170	Direct
Insurance - Property	-	-	1	-	1	Direct
Taxes - Property	4	4	2	2	12	Direct
Aircraft - Company	175	15	60	50	300	Distribution
Depreciation	14	29	10	4	57	Direct
Salary Continuation & Pension	20	5	13	7	45	Direct
Fixed Social Security	15	4	10	7	36	Direct
Hospital & Group Insurance	13	3	9	6	31	Direct
Employee Education & Training	9	2	6	4	21	Direct
Office Maintenance & Repair	2	2	1	1	6	Direct
Electric Power	8	8	4	4	24	Office Square Ft.
Workmen's Compensation	1	1	1	1	4	Direct
Unemployment Compensation	2	1	2	1	6	Direct
Data Processing Rent & Supplies	50	6	54	31	141	Computer Hours
Legal Fees	-	-	12	5	17	Direct
Professional Services/Consultants	8	4	9	10	31	Direct
Auditors	-	-	15	3	18	Direct
Association Fees (CRI & ACI)	11	2	12	5	30	Salary Employees
Dues & Subscriptions	4	2	3	1	10	Direct
Office Equipment Rent	-	-	8	-	8	Direct
Postage	22	-	8	6	36	Direct
Telephone & Telegraph	27	2	10	6	45	Direct
Office Supplies (Inc. Printing)	18	-	10	4	32	Direct
Outside Printing	24	-	12	-	36	Direct
Advertising & Promotion	250	-	-	25	275	Direct
Sample Loss	65	-	-	-	65	Direct
Donations	-	-	12	12	24	Direct
Materials & Supplies	-	160	-	-	160	Direct
Branch Offices	120	-	-	-	120	Direct
TOTAL	$1,718	$363	$ 631	$ 280	$2,992	

FIGURE 8-3

SUMMARY OF FIXED EXPENSES

sistent with the firm's long-range plans and short-run objectives. These costs should be analyzed through a system of numbered project requests for top management approval. These requests should state the purpose, estimated hours, equipment requirements, and other expenses. These requests can then be evaluated versus potential results of the project—cost reduction, new products, and existing product improvements. This provides management a method to determine where research effort is being directed and an analysis of the cost of each project as compared to the initial budget.

Control of R & D cost does not restrict research personnel. It does provide a systematic approach for top management analysis and decisions on research resources.

Continuous management attention is required to the area of research and development project selection and expenses. Often, R & D personnel tend to work on projects which are interesting, rather than those which will contribute to the long-run objectives of the firm.

Sample Expense

In certain industries, such as home furnishings, the cost for samples of products for dealers or prospective customers can be an important cost, both for introducing a new product and maintaining an existing line.

For the firm being simulated in this book, a Sample Department is maintained to prepare, package, ship, and administer samples of carpet for dealer displays. In this case, Figure 8-4 shows where a certain amount of the sample cost is recovered due to the sale of samples to dealers.

The Sample Department should be budgeted and controlled similar to other manufacturing departments. However, the loss on samples is considered a selling and marketing expense. A cost sheet should be prepared for each sample stockkeeping item.

Separation by Channel of Distribution

For proper profit analysis and control by channel of distribution, expenses must be separated by these channels. Large volume accounts which require little sales effort and which create few transactions, result in lower costs than multiple retail accounts with numerous small volume orders.

An example of the separation of costs for sales and marketing is shown in Figure 8-5. A portion of salaries and bonuses are directly related to the channel of distribution. Sales management salaries must be separated on an empirical basis; such as, percent of sales.

In this example, a higher proportion of company aircraft expense is charged to the large volume channel of distribution. It is likely that these aircraft will be utilized more frequently with the large volume buyers, either visiting or servicing their requirements, or transporting them to manufacturing locations or distribution points.

One of the larger expenses which is charged to the retail channel of distribution is advertising. In most cases, the majority of advertising expenses is related to the retail channel of distribution. However, if the firm name or product name is being used on the

Expense	Budget
Salaries & Benefits	$15,000
Labor	40,000
Material	150,000
Operating Supplies	20,000
Packaging Materials	40,000
Postage & Freight	24,000
Other Expenses	16,000
Total	$305,000
Revenue From Sales of Samples	240,000
Net Loss on Samples	$ 65,000

FIGURE 8-4
SAMPLE DEPARTMENT BUDGET

items for the large volume channel of distribution, a portion of the advertising expenses is directly related to these larger customers.

Sometimes, there is a feeling that it is not necessary to separate these fixed expenses by channel of distribution. On this basis, the contribution to profit and fixed cost is the criteria for management decisions. Yet, managers must have a reasonable indication of what fixed expenses are by channel of distribution in order to determine the desired contribution rate for target pricing and analysis.

There are also the legal implications of price differential by volume, channel of distribution, or customer. These factors change with legislation, and prices must be evaluated in the light of current laws. Regardless of the final price derived—whether based on the market, the laws, or the cost—managers must know their real cost, differentiated by significant characteristics for evaluating customers, markets, or trade channels.

Similarly, broad distribution and higher sales growth cannot be achieved by con-

Account	Large Volume Customers	Retail Customers	Total	Basis For Distribution
Salaries & Bonus	$ 72	$640	$ 712	Direct & Sales
Travel Expense - Auto & Commercial	14	130	144	Direct & Sales
Taxes Property	1	3	4	Sales
Aircraft - Company	65	110	175	Sales
Depreciation	4	10	14	Sales
Salary Continuation & Pension			⎰20	Sal. & Bonus $
Fixed Social Security	6	51	15	Sal. & Bonus $
Hospital & Group Insurance			13	Sal. & Bonus $
Employee Educ. & Training			⎱9	Sal. & Bonus $
Office Maintenance & Repair	2	8	⎰2	Sales
Electric Power			⎱8	Sales
Workmen's Compensation	1	2	⎰1	Sal. & Bonus $
Unemployment Compensation			⎱2	Sal. & Bonus $
Data Processing Rent & Supp.	8	42	50	Transactions
Prof. Services/Consultants	2	6	8	Sales
Association Fees	2	13	⎰11	Sales
Dues & Subscriptions			⎱4	Sales
Postage	2	20	22	Transactions
Telephone & Telegraph	4	23	27	Direct
Office Supplies (Inc.Printing)	2	16	18	Direct
Outside Printing	-	24	24	Direct
Advertising	-	250	250	Sales
Sample Loss	-	65	65	Sales
Branch Offices	-	120	120	Sales
TOTAL	$185	$1,533	$1,718	

FIGURE 8-5

DISTRIBUTION OF SALES AND MARKETING EXPENSE

centration on the one or two channels of distribution which may have the highest contribution rate and a low volume potential. It is, of course, true that sales volume is important. Yet, many firms still find excellent profits with lower volumes provided products are properly priced in the market place.

The costs calculated in this text are for substantial volumes per production run. Where volumes vary widely or some are small per production order, special calculations may be required by volume range. Low volume items result in increased in-process or material losses, set-up cost, distribution, potential obsolescence, and the cost of handling additional administrative transactions. Where the cost for samples, advertising, or similar expenses are significant for introducing or discontinuing a product, these costs may be estimated by volume range. In the years ahead, managers may find their product lines becoming more complex as the needs of consumers continue to change.

A summary of the fixed expenses by channel of distribution is shown in Figure 8-6.

Fixed Expenses - $000

	Large Volume Customers	Retail Customers	Total
Sales & Marketing	$185	$1,533	$1,718
R & D	72	291	363
Administration - Division & Corporate	111	800	911
TOTAL	$368	$2,624	$2,992

FIGURE 8-6

FIXED EXPENSES BY CHANNEL OF DISTRIBUTION

Calculation of Cost Sheet Values

Now that these expenses have been determined, values must be determined for cost sheet application.

For selling and marketing, the best basis may be total first quality manufacturing costs for the normal volume sales. This can be determined by the expected normal volume per item multiplied by the calculated first quality manufacturing cost and accumulated for all items.

This method approaches a percent of sales mark-up. At this point in the cost sheet calculation, the percent of manufacturing cost is easier to determine. Then, the mark-up on manufacturing cost for the two channels of distribution is:

$$\text{Selling \& Marketing Expense Multiplier} = \frac{\text{Selling \& Marketing Expense}}{\text{Manufacturing Cost}}$$

$$\text{Retail Mark-up} = \frac{\text{Retail Selling \& Marketing Expense}}{\text{Retail Manufacturing Cost}}$$

$$= \frac{\$1,533,000}{\$14,178,000}$$

$$= 0.108$$

$$\text{Large Volume Mark-up} = \frac{\text{Large Volume Selling \& Marketing Expense}}{\text{Large Volume Manufacturing Cost}}$$

$$= \frac{\$ \quad 185,000}{\$ \quad 3,545,000}$$

$$= \quad 0.052$$

The cost sheet values (Figure 8-7, line number 23) are:

Retail $= \quad \$2.440 \quad \times \quad 0.108 \quad = \quad \$0.264$

Large Volume $= \quad \$2.440 \quad \times \quad 0.052 \quad = \quad \$0.127$

The higher cost for the retail channel of distribution results from the advertising, salesmen, and other costs associated with lower volume of the many individual retail accounts.

Care should be attached to the development of an advertising budget and it's distribution to channels of distribution. In many cases, this item must be held in the corporate or total fixed cost without distribution. The high cost and inability to adequately relate advertising to a specific trade channel distorts total cost calculations in the short run. Where this or other similar significant expenses exist, contribution analysis is the best short-run guide for decisions.

Advertising should be planned well in advance for budget purposes. Requests for advertising expenditures should include media cost, frequency, expected results, and a method to follow up to determine if planned objectives were achieved. Consumer surveys and similar techniques are useful for follow-up. Advertising resources should be expended only for specific objectives based on sound business policies.

The utilization of a percent gives a higher cost value for higher price items. Though this may be subject to discussion, the number of units sold per order tends to decrease with higher prices. Often, too, additional sales service may be required for higher priced units. As an example, the selling and marketing costs for selling a high priced car is more per unit sold than a mass market vehicle.

Similar multipliers and cost sheet values for research and development (Figure 8-8, line number 24) are:

		Multiplier	*Cost Sheet Value*
Retail	=	0.020	$0.048
Large Volume	=	0.020	$0.048

Some managers have calculated cost or priced large volume channels of distribution as plus business; and therefore, they have not assigned any research and development cost to this channel. This has forced the retail or other channels to carry the cost for research and development. In many cases, the item would not have been available to the large volume buyer if it had not been developed either for their requirement or for the requirement of other customers.

Managers must insist that mail order, private label, and other large volume channels of distribution pay their own way with Research and Development cost.

PRODUCT COST SHEET

PLANT	DIVISION	SPEC. NC.	PRODUCT NO.	PRODUCT NAME	CAL. NC.
ATLANTA	HOME FURNISHINGS	501	201	ALL AMERICAN	6102

CAL. BY + DATE	CHECKED BY	MATERIAL WT. 1,280 LB.	MACHINE 5/32 LOOP	SPI 7.0	SPEC. INSTR. NONE

ITEM	LINE	ITEM	UNIT	SPEC. NC.	STD. UNITS	MAT. MULT.	ALWD. UNITS	STD. PRICE	VARIABLE	FIXED	TOTAL
MATERIALS	1	YARN	LB	110	1.280	1.035	1.325	1.170	1.551	X.XXX	1.551
	2	OUTSIDE PROCESS	XX	XXX	X.XXX	X.XXX	X.XXX	X.XXX	X.XXX	X.XXX	X.XXX
	3	FIRST BACK	SY	224	1.000	1.020	1.020	0.200	0.204	X.XXX	0.204
	4	DYE + CHEMICALS	LB	980	1.850	1.075	1.990	0.028	0.056	X.XXX	0.056
	5	ADHESIVE	LB	214	1.625	1.050	1.710	0.080	0.137	X.XXX	0.137
	6	SECOND BACK	SY	225	1.000	1.020	1.020	0.160	0.163	X.XXX	0.163
	7	PACKAGE	SY	9210	1.000	1.025	1.025	0.030	0.031	X.XXX	0.031
	8	SUB-TOTAL; MATERIAL COST							2.142	X.XXX	2.142
MANUFACTURING	9	RECEIVE + TUFT		$15.00 V	$10.00 F	0.45 MH	100 UNITS		0.068	0.045	0.113
	10	DYE		8.22 V	2.96 F	0.60 MH	100 UNITS		0.049	0.018	0.067
	11	DRY		27.00 V	11.00 F	0.07 MH	100 UNITS		0.019	0.008	0.027
	12	ADHESIVE		30.00 V	21.00 F	0.06 MH	100 UNITS		0.018	0.013	0.031
	13	OUTSIDE PROCESS		V	F	MH	UNITS		X.XXX	X.XXX	X.XXX
	14	INSPECT + PACK		25.00 V	20.00 F	0.06 MH	100 UNITS		0.015	0.012	0.027
	15	SHIP		1.96 V	2.38 F	0.75 MH	100 UNITS		0.015	0.018	0.033
	16	SUB-TOTAL; MANUFACTURING COST - FIRST QUALITY							2.326	0.114	2.440
QUALITY	17	PLANT OFF-QUALITY 0.0200 X LINE 16							0.047	0.002	0.049
	18	CLAIMS + RETURNS 0.0050 X LINE 16							0.012	0.001	0.013
	19	POLICY ADJUSTMENT 0.0025 X LINE 16							0.006	0.000	0.006
	20	SUB-TOTAL; MANUFACTURING COST - AVERAGE QUALITY							2.391	0.117	2.508

ITEM	LINE	DISTRIBUTION, SELLING, RESEARCH AND ADMINISTRATIVE EXPENSES	LARGE VOLUME VARIABLE	LARGE VOLUME TOTAL	RETAIL VARIABLE	RETAIL TOTAL
	21	SUB-TOTAL; MANUFACTURING COST - AVERAGE QUALITY	2.391	2.508	2.391	2.508
SELLING	22	DISTRIBUTION SERVICES COST PER UNIT	0.002	0.052	0.063	0.138
+	23	SELLING + MARKETING 0.052 + 0.108 X LINE 16	0.000	0.127	0.000	0.264
OTHER	24	RESEARCH + DEVELOPMENT 0.020 X LINE 16	0.000	0.048	0.000	0.048
	25	ADMINISTRATION 0.031 + 0.056 X LINE 16	0.000	0.076	0.000	0.136
	26	TOTAL; COST + NET BREAKEVEN PRICE	2.391	2.811	2.454	3.094

FIGURE 8-7
SELLING AND MARKETING COST CALCULATION

PRODUCT COST SHEET

PLANT ATLANTA	DIVISION HOME FURNISHINGS	SPEC. NO. 501	PRODUCT NO. 201	PRODUCT NAME ALL AMERICAN	CAL. NO. 6102

CAL. BY + DATE	CHECKED BY	MATERIAL WT. 1,280 LB.	MACHINE 5/32 LOOP	SPI 7.0	SPEC. INSTR. NONE

ITEM	LINE	ITEM	UNIT	SPEC. NO.	STD. UNITS	MAT. MULT.	ALWD. UNITS	STD. PRICE	COST PER UNIT (SQ. YD.) VARIABLE	FIXED	TOTAL
MATERIALS	1	YARN	LB	110	1.280	1.035	1.325	1.170	1.551	X.XXX	1.551
	2	OUTSIDE PROCESS	XX	XXX	X.XXX	X.XXX	X.XXX	X.XXX	X.XXX	X.XXX	X.XXX
	3	FIRST BACK	SY	224	1.000	1.020	1.020	0.200	0.204	X.XXX	0.204
	4	DYE + CHEMICALS	LB	980	1.850	1.075	1.990	0.028	0.056	X.XXX	0.056
	5	ADHESIVE	LB	214	1.625	1.050	1.710	0.080	0.137	X.XXX	0.137
	6	SECOND BACK	SY	225	1.000	1.020	1.020	0.160	0.163	X.XXX	0.163
	7	PACKAGE	SY	9210	1.000	1.025	1.025	0.030	0.031	X.XXX	0.031
	8	SUB-TOTAL: MATERIAL COST							2.142	X.XXX	2.142
MANUFACTURING	9	RECEIVE + TUFT		$15.00 V	$10.00 F	0.45 MH	100 UNITS		0.068	0.045	0.113
	10	DYE		8.22 V	2.96 F	0.60 MH	100 UNITS		0.049	0.018	0.067
	11	DRY		27.00 V	11.00 F	0.07 MH	100 UNITS		0.019	0.008	0.027
	12	ADHESIVE		30.00 V	21.00 F	0.06 MH	100 UNITS		0.018	0.013	0.031
	13	OUTSIDE PROCESS		V	F	MH	UNITS		X.XXX	X.XXX	X.XXX
	14	INSPECT + PACK		25.00 V	20.00 F	0.06 MH	100 UNITS		0.015	0.012	0.027
	15	SHIP		1.96 V	2.38 F	0.75 MH	100 UNITS		0.015	0.018	0.033
	16	SUB-TOTAL: MANUFACTURING COST - FIRST QUALITY							2.326	0.114	2.440
QUALITY	17	PLANT OFF-QUALITY 0.0200 X LINE 16							0.047	0.002	0.049
	18	CLAIMS + RETURNS 0.0050 X LINE 16							0.012	0.001	0.013
	19	POLICY ADJUSTMENT 0.0025 X LINE 16							0.006	0.000	0.006
	20	SUB-TOTAL: MANUFACTURING COST - AVERAGE QUALITY							2.391	0.117	2.508

ITEM	LINE	DISTRIBUTION, SELLING, RESEARCH AND ADMINISTRATIVE EXPENSES	LARGE VOLUME VARIABLE	TOTAL	RETAIL VARIABLE	TOTAL
	21	SUB-TOTAL: MANUFACTURING COST - AVERAGE QUALITY	2.391	2.508	2.391	2.508
SELLING, ETC.	22	DISTRIBUTION SERVICES	0.002	0.052	0.063	0.138
	23	SELLING + MARKETING 0.052 + 0.108 X LINE 16	0.000	0.127	0.000	0.264
	24	RESEARCH + DEVELOPMENT 0.020 X LINE 16	0.000	0.048	0.000	0.048
	25	ADMINISTRATION 0.031 + 0.056 X LINE 16	0.000	0.076	0.000	0.136
	26	TOTAL: COST + NET BREAKEVEN PRICE	2.391	2.811	2.454	3.094

FIGURE 8-8

CALCULATION OF TOTAL COST AND NET BREAKEVEN PRICE

The administrative multipliers and cost sheet values (Figure 8-8, line number 25) are:

		Multiplier	*Cost Sheet Value*
Retail	=	0.056	$0.136
Large Volume	=	0.031	$0.076

Since most of the administrative expenses which are caused by transactions—such as accounts receivable, inventory auditing, and others—were separated by the transactions or other cause of costs, this cost mark-up has a relationship to a cost per unit for administrative expenses. In some situations, administrative expenses for transactions may be on a per unit basis with the remainder calculated as indicated.

The total cost and net break-even price, as calculated in Figure 8-8, is determined by channel of distribution.

Calculation of Standard Profit

Profit mark-up may be based on percent of sales, return on investment, or some other basis. A percent of sales basis is easy and it is a common guide for measuring the relative success of businesses. A better basis is the manager's objective return on gross replacement value investment.

First, determine the investments for the firm's expected normal volume, as shown in Figure 8-9. For raw materials, work-in-process, and finished goods inventory, these can be determined by calculation from statistical forecasting and production scheduling systems. Accounts receivable is related to the terms of sale.

Plant, property, and equipment can be estimated from the Depreciation Worksheet (Figure 5-6) for inclusion in Figure 8-9. Often, investment determinations must be made by channel of distribution and then sub-divided by certain products or methods of manufacture depending on their specific requirements. In this case, Product Line A (Figure 8-9) requires a greater utilization of plant, property, and equipment. Due to shorter runs and other production characteristics, higher investments are required relative to sales volume.

Given a management target of twenty-five percent return on gross investment, as illustrated in Figure 2-1, the target profit required may be calculated. As an example, the investment for retail customers, Product Line A is $2,740,000. A 25 percent return on this investment before taxes will require a profit of $685,000 annually, as indicated in Figure 5-6. Should income tax rates vary over the long term, the profit objective may be stated as after tax; then, add the expected taxes to obtain the total profit target.

Frequently, management will make a financial decision to borrow money rather than make an investment in the business. The cost of interest may be charged to administrative expense, or separated as a specific item. In any event, the decision to borrow or invest is a financial one. When money is borrowed and interest is charged to cost, the return on investment profit requirements must be reduced by the interest expense.

	Retail Customers		Large Volume Customers		
	Product A	Product B	Product A	Product B	Total
Raw Materials					
Retail - Product A	$ 185				$ 185
Retail - Product B		$ 345			345
Large Volume			$ 45	$ 85	130
Work-In-Process					
Retail - Product A	85				85
Retail - Product B		175			175
Large Volume			20	45	65
Finished Goods					
Retail - Product A	570				570
Retail - Product B		575			575
Large Volume			45	100	145
Cash	135	265	30	70	500
Accounts Receivable:					
Retail	480	850			1,330
Large Volume			85	170	255
Plant & Equipment Exc. Dyeing & Drying	1,285	2,560	320	640	4,805
Dyeing & Drying	-	855	-	215	1,070
Total Investment	$2,740	$5,625	$ 545	$1,325	$10,235
Target Profit Required for 25% Return on Investment	$ 685	$1,405	$ 135	$ 330	$ 2,555

FIGURE 8-9

CALCULATION OF INVESTMENT AND TARGET PROFIT

Management cannot expect to recover interest expense and return on investment based on the gross replacement value and remain competitive with market prices.

For evaluating investment opportunities, the discounted cash flow should be included in the analysis. Utilization of this technique enables managers to estimate the present value of future incomes.

Tables for the present worth values of $1 are available in published texts at various interest or return on investment rates. In an inflationary time of high or rising interest rates, this type analysis is extremely important in determining the optimum alternative for limited investment resources.

An example of the present value of projected net cash income for four years is:

Year "n"	Forecasted Net Cash Income	Present Value of $1 Receivable after "n" Periods with Interest at 25 Percent	Present Value of Net Cash Income
1	$ 20,000	0.800	$16,000
2	24,000	0.640	15,360
3	30,000	0.512	15,360
4	40,000	0.410	16,400
	$114,000		$63,120

Assuming a desired rate of twenty-five percent return on investment, a maximum $63,120 can be invested now based on a five year forecast of $114,000 net cash income.

Now that target profit has been estimated, a method must be used to determine values per item for cost sheet application. Though some use percent of sales, percent of manufacturing costs, and other techniques, a percent of conversion costs may be a better basis. Conversion costs which are the total first quality manufacturing costs for the normal volume less material costs, is an indicator of the time value of plant, and facilities, or other resources utilized.

A percent of sales or manufacturing cost mark-up indicates a higher profit requirement due to material cost. This factor is included in the investment calculations. Often, product investment determination must be separated by price range.

The profit mark-up or multiplier is:

$$\text{Profit Multiplier} = \frac{\text{Target Profit Required}}{\text{Standard Conversion Cost}}$$

For the simulated firm, channels of distribution, and product lines, these are:

	Large Volume Customers Product A	Product B	Retail Customers Product A	Product B
Profit Required	$135	$330	$685	$1,405
Conversion Cost	75	270	290	1,100
Profit Multiplier	1.80	1.22	2.36	1.28

With this method, there is a small difference in the profit requirements for large volume as compared to the retail channel of distribution. In some systems, managers will mark-up large volume customers; say ten percent, and retail, say fifteen percent, which indicates a much higher profit requirement for retail channel of distribution. The real difference in many of these channels is cost, not profit requirements to generate a return-on-investment. *(Large volume channel of distribution must generate a reasonable return on investment.)*

The cost sheet values (Figure 8-10, line number 27) for Product Number 201, which is Product Line B, are:

	Large Volume Customer	Retail Customer
Total First Quality Manufacturing Costs =	$2.440	$2.440
Less Materials Costs =	2.142	2.142
Conversion Costs =	$0.298	$0.298
Profit Mark-up =	1.22	1.28
Standard Profit =	$0.364	$0.381

In many cases, a percent of sales has been used as a method to estimate *target*. This is a common guide for measuring the relative relationship between firms. It is an easy way to obtain a mathematical calculation. However, where the firm has a wide variety of products, and channels of distribution, a percent of sales may not adequately reflect the profit required for return on investment. In most cases where percent of sales has been used, this method will indicate a much lower profit requirement for large volume channels of distribution than the technique of return-on-investment. (The net target selling prices are shown in Figure 8-10, line number 28 for Product Number 201.)

Terms and Other Price Markdowns

Given, the net target price has been calculated, the total target selling price may be calculated to include terms, discounts, obsolescence costs, and selling price markdowns.

For the simulated firm, terms are five percent cash or net thirty days for retail accounts; and net thirty days for large volume accounts. Therefore, a cash discount is included in the retail channel of distribution calculation.

The obsolescence loss for retail is one percent of sales. This loss results from making products to stock with the resultant obsolescence costs due to colors, or models which must be sold at a reduced price when colors or models are discontinued. Since the large volume accounts are *made to order* or *inventory is guaranteed,* no obsolescence cost is included.

In actual practice, obsolescence cost or markdown in sales can be determined by separating all obsolete or discontinued items sold and:

$$\text{Obsolescence Cost} = \left[\text{Standard Price} - \text{Price for Obsolete Item}\right] \times \text{Number of Items Sold}$$

PRODUCT COST SHEET

PLANT ATLANTA	DIVISION HOME FURNISHINGS	SPEC. NO. 501	PRODUCT NO. 201	PRODUCT NAME ALL AMERICAN	CAL. NO. 6102
CAL. BY + DATE	CHECKED BY	MATERIAL WT. 1,280 LB.	MACHINE 5/32 LOOP	SPI 7.0 SPEC. INSTR. NONE	

ITEM	LINE	ITEM	UNIT	SPEC. NO.	STD. UNITS	MAT. MULT.	ALWD. UNITS	STD. PRICE	COST PER UNIT (SQ. YD.) VARIABLE	FIXED	TOTAL
MATERIALS	1	YARN	LB	110	1,280	1,035	1,325	1,170	1,551	X.XXX	1,551
	2	OUTSIDE PROCESS	XX	XXX	X.XXX	X.XXX	X.XXX	X.XXX	X.XXX	X.XXX	X.XXX
	3	FIRST BACK	SY	224	1,000	1,020	1,020	0,200	0,204	X.XXX	0,204
	4	DYE + CHEMICALS	LB	980	1,850	1,075	1,990	0,028	0,056	X.XXX	0,056
	5	ADHESIVE	LB	214	1,625	1,050	1,710	0,080	0,137	X.XXX	0,137
	6	SECOND BACK	SY	225	1,000	1,020	1,020	0,160	0,163	X.XXX	0,163
	7	PACKAGE	SY	9210	1,000	1,025	1,025	0,030	0,031	X.XXX	0,031
	8	SUB-TOTAL: MATERIAL COST							2,142	X.XXX	2,142
MANUFACTURING	9	RECEIVE + TUFT		$15.00 V	$10.00 F	0.45 MH	100 UNITS		0,068	0,045	0,113
	10	DYE		8.22 V	2.96 F	0.60 MH	100 UNITS		0,049	0,018	0,067
	11	DRY		27.00 V	11.00 F	0.07 MH	100 UNITS		0,019	0,008	0,027
	12	ADHESIVE		30.00 V	21.00 F	0.06 MH	100 UNITS		0,018	0,013	0,031
	13	OUTSIDE PROCESS		V	F	MH	UNITS		X.XXX	X.XXX	X.XXX
	14	INSPECT + PACK		25.00 V	20.00 F	0.06 MH	100 UNITS		0,015	0,012	0,027
	15	SHIP		1.96 V	2.38 F	0.75 MH	100 UNITS		0,015	0,018	0,033
	16	SUB-TOTAL: MANUFACTURING COST - FIRST QUALITY							2,326	0,114	2,440
QUALITY	17	PLANT OFF-QUALITY 0.0200 X LINE 16							0,047	0,002	0,049
	18	CLAIMS + RETURNS 0.0050 X LINE 16							0,012	0,001	0,013
	19	POLICY ADJUSTMENT 0.0025 X LINE 16							0,006	0,000	0,006
	20	SUB-TOTAL: MANUFACTURING COST - AVERAGE QUALITY							2,391	0,117	2,508

ITEM	LINE	DISTRIBUTION, SELLING, RESEARCH AND ADMINISTRATIVE EXPENSES	LARGE VOLUME VARIABLE	TOTAL	RETAIL VARIABLE	TOTAL
	21	SUB-TOTAL: MANUFACTURING COST - AVERAGE QUALITY	2,391	2,508	2,391	2,508
SELLING	22	DISTRIBUTION SERVICES	0,002	0,052	0,063	0,138
	23	SELLING + MARKETING 0.052 + 0.108 X LINE 16	0,000	0,127	0,000	0,264
	24	RESEARCH + DEVELOPMENT 0.020 X LINE 16	0,000	0,048	0,000	0,048
	25	ADMINISTRATION 0.031 + 0.056 X LINE 16	0,000	0,076	0,000	0,136
	26	TOTAL: COST + NET BREAKEVEN PRICE	2,391	2,811	2,454	3,094
DISCOUNTS PROFIT	27	TARGET PROFIT - 25% RETURN ON GROSS REPLACEMENT VALUE	0,364	0,364	0,381	0,381
	28	TOTAL: NET TARGET SELLING PRICE	2,755	3,175	2,835	3,475
	29	TERMS OR CASH DISCOUNT				
	30	OBSOLESCENCE LOSS				
	31	TOTAL: GROSS TARGET SELLING PRICE				

FIGURE 8-10

CALCULATION OF NET TARGET SELLING PRICE

Here, too, a budget should be set for the number of units expected to become obsolete and a standard price for the obsolete item. In this way, both quantity and price obsolescence variances can be determined. The cost of obsolescence is a significant part of the cost of carrying inventory items with a season, model year, or other cycle. A hypothetical actual cost of carrying inventory scale may be:

	Large Volume Items	Medium Volume Items	Low Volume Items
Cost of Money	7.5	7.5	7.5
Warehouse Expense	1.0	1.5	2.5
Obsolescence	1.0	3.0	5.0
Administrative Expense	1.5	1.5	1.5
Total	11.0	13.5	16.5

For normal inventory levels, the cost of money is recovered from the profit mark-up required for a return on investment in inventory.

The total *target* selling prices are shown in Figure 8-11, line number 31. The *target* selling price is exactly that—a *target* or *guide*. It is the price which based on normal volume will generate management's objective profit. *It is not expected to be the exact selling price.* It is not intended to restrict management judgment in setting market prices. (The relationship of costs and prices is illustrated in cartoon form in Figure 8-12.)

With these data it is possible to calculate the *target* contribution by channel of distribution. For Product Number 201, these are:

	Large Volume Customer	Retail Customer
Net Target Selling Price =	$3.175	$3.475
Less Total Variable Costs =	2.393	2.454
Contribution =	0.782	1.021
Contribution percent of Net Target Selling Price =	24.6%	29.4%

These data indicate that the contribution, the amount of money received for our products in excess of variable cost, must be approximately 4.8% (29.4 − 24.6) higher on the retail channel of distribution to recover fixed cost at normal volume and generate the target profit.

In some situations, it may not be important to calculate fixed expenses due to errors in distribution, allocation or normal volumes. This direct or variable costing logic implies that the contribution amount or rate is the guide to management decisions, and much of this is good. The calculation of fixed cost is not intended to imply that the data derived will necessarily be the legally accepted basis for price bracket differentials. In the event of a court test, the more precisely defined, logically correct, and valid cost basis presented will significantly affect the resulting decision of the courts. Yet, managers

PRODUCT COST SHEET

PLANT ATLANTA	DIVISION HOME FURNISHINGS	SPEC. NO. 501	PRODUCT NO. 201	PRODUCT NAME ALL AMERICAN	CAL. NO. 61C2
CAL. BY + DATE	CHECKED BY	MATERIAL WT. 1,280 LB.	MACHINE 5/32 LOOP	SPI 7.0 SPEC. INSTR. NONE	

ITEM	LINE	ITEM	UNIT	SPEC. NO.	STD. UNITS	MAT. MULT.	ALWD. UNITS	STD. PRICE	COST PER UNIT (SQ. YD.) VARIABLE	FIXED	TOTAL
MATERIALS	1	YARN	LB	110	1.280	1.035	1.325	1.170	1.551	X.XXX	1.551
	2	OUTSIDE PROCESS	XX	XXX	X.XXX	X.XXX	X.XXX	X.XXX	X.XXX	X.XXX	X.XXX
	3	FIRST BACK	SY	224	1.000	1.020	1.020	0.200	0.204	X.XXX	0.204
	4	DYE + CHEMICALS	LB	980	1.850	1.075	1.990	0.028	0.056	X.XXX	0.056
	5	ADHESIVE	LB	214	1.625	1.050	1.710	0.080	0.137	X.XXX	0.137
	6	SECOND BACK	SY	225	1.000	1.020	1.020	0.160	0.163	X.XXX	0.163
	7	PACKAGE	SY	9210	1.000	1.025	1.025	0.030	0.031	X.XXX	0.031
	8	SUB-TOTAL: MATERIAL COST							2.142	X.XXX	2.142
MANUFACTURING	9	RECEIVE + TUFT		$15.00 V	$10.00 F	0.45 MH	100 UNITS		0.068	0.045	0.113
	10	DYE		8.22 V	2.96 F	0.60 MH	100 UNITS		0.049	0.018	0.067
	11	DRY		27.00 V	11.00 F	0.07 MH	100 UNITS		0.019	0.008	0.027
	12	ADHESIVE		30.00 V	21.00 F	0.06 MH	100 UNITS		0.018	0.013	0.031
	13	OUTSIDE PROCESS		V	F	MH	UNITS		X.XXX	X.XXX	X.XXX
	14	INSPECT + PACK		25.00 V	20.00 F	0.06 MH	100 UNITS		0.015	0.012	0.027
	15	SHIP		1.96 V	2.38 F	0.75 MH	100 UNITS		0.015	0.018	0.033
	16	SUB-TOTAL: MANUFACTURING COST – FIRST QUALITY							2.326	0.114	2.440
QUALITY	17	PLANT OFF-QUALITY 0.0200 X LINE 16							0.047	0.002	0.049
	18	CLAIMS + RETURNS 0.0050 X LINE 16							0.012	0.001	0.013
	19	POLICY ADJUSTMENT 0.0025 X LINE 16							0.006	0.000	0.006
	20	SUB-TOTAL: MANUFACTURING COST – AVERAGE QUALITY							2.391	0.117	2.508

ITEM	LINE	DISTRIBUTION, SELLING, RESEARCH AND ADMINISTRATIVE EXPENSES	LARGE VOLUME VARIABLE	TOTAL	RETAIL VARIABLE	TOTAL
	21	SUB-TOTAL: MANUFACTURING COST – AVERAGE QUALITY	2.391	2.508	2.391	2.508
S + SELLING	22	DISTRIBUTION SERVICES COST PER UNIT	0.002	0.052	0.063	0.138
	23	SELLING + MARKETING 0.052 + 0.108 X LINE 16	0.000	0.127	0.000	0.264
	24	RESEARCH + DEVELOPMENT 0.020 X LINE 16	0.000	0.048	0.000	0.048
	25	ADMINISTRATION 0.031 + 0.056 X LINE 16	0.000	0.076	0.000	0.136
	26	TOTAL: COST + NET BREAKEVEN PRICE	2.391	2.811	2.454	3.094
D + DISCOUNTS PROFIT	27	TARGET PROFIT – 25% RETURN ON GROSS REPLACEMENT VALUE	0.364	0.364	0.381	0.381
	28	TOTAL: NET TARGET SELLING PRICE	2.755	3.175	2.835	3.475
	29	TERMS OR CASH DISCOUNT 0.000 + 0.050 X LINE 31	0.000	0.000	0.149	0.185
	30	OBSOLESCENCE LOSS 0.000 + 0.010 X LINE 31	0.000	0.000	0.032	0.037
	31	TOTAL: GROSS TARGET SELLING PRICE	2.755	3.175	3.016	3.697

FIGURE 8-11

CALCULATION OF GROSS TARGET SELLING PRICE

FIGURE 8-12
COST AND PRICES—MANAGER'S VIEWPOINT

must set objectives or targets by product and channel of distribution, and then strive to achieve these targets. Total cost calculations should be available for information and analysis.

An example of a chemical product cost sheet for a Canadian manufacturer illustrating the application of transaction cost, price breaks, and geographical zone pricing is shown in Figure 8-13.

```
PRCDUCT CODE:  23-01-10    DESCRIPTION:  CONCRETE FLOOR FINISH
CCNTAINER CODE:   11       DESCRIPTION:  CASE - 1 GALLON CANS      UNIT OF MEASURE:  GALLON
STANDARD BATCH SIZE:  1,500 GALLONS     WEIGHT PER UNIT OF MEASURE:  9.500
```

	COST BY PRICE BREAK				PACKAGING SPECIFICATION:
	A	B	C	D	44-01
RAW MATERIAL COST	2.020				
PACKAGING MATERIAL	.313				
VARIABLE COST					
RECEIVING	.002				
WEIGH AND MIX	.001				
CAN AND CARTON PRINTING	.000				
PACKAGING	.010				
WAREHOUSING	.010				
MAINTENANCE	.012				
SHIPPING	.051				
CTHER	.000				
INSPECTION CHARGE	.003				
SLB-TOTAL: VARIABLE COST	2.422				
FIXED COST					
MANUFACTURING	.128	.128	.128	.128	
SELLING: TRANSACTION	.245	.167	.132	.050	
SELLING: OTHER	.605	.605	.605	.605	
ADMINISTRATION: TRANSACTION	.637	.436	.344	.130	
ADMINISTRATION: OTHER	.403	.403	.403	.403	
TCTAL COST	4.440	4.161	4.034	3.738	
CCMMISSIONS + BONUSES	1.091	.965	.909	.775	
TARGET PROFIT	.965	.854	.804	.686	
SLB-TOTAL: TARGET SELLING PRICE	6.496	5.980	5.747	5.199	
DISTRIBUTION COST ZONE 1	.515	.292	.183	.160	
ZONE 2	.578	.307	.237	.298	
ZONE 3	.675	.387	.268	.327	
TCTAL TARGET SELLING PRICE					
ZONE 1	7.011	6.272	5.930	5.359	
ZONE 2	7.074	6.287	5.984	5.497	
ZONE 3	7.171	6.367	6.015	5.526	

FIGURE 8-13
CHEMICAL PRODUCT COST SHEET

At this point, the costs which have been estimated are for standard conditions of manufacturing performance, product mix, and normal volume. Under certain conditions, the elements of fixed cost and profit can be different. Most all calculations or estimates of any type are wrong to some extent. The only important question for managers is whether they are *significantly* wrong. In the following two chapters, methods will be utilized to point out how these differences and their significance can be estimated.

On some occasions, particularly where actual variable costs vary significantly from standard variable costs, it may be necessary to calculate both standard and actual costs for management's consideration. For this purpose, once the variance has been determined by item, cost center, and its relationship as a percent of standard cost, this percent may be multiplied times the standard cost to convert the standard cost to an actual cost estimate. In situations where this information is required, it may be necessary to add additional columns to the standard cost sheet and prepare the calculations from standard to actual cost on a routine basis.

SUMMARY

The determination of selling, marketing, research, development, and administrative expenses by channel of distribution is an essential element of an effective business plan.

The chart of accounts should be constructed to separate an expense based on the cause of the expense. Proper definition of accounts reduces the need for allocation or distribution of expenses to departments, divisions, or channels of distribution. Variable budgeting is illustrated as an essential technique for proper control of expenses and accurate funds forecast.

The handling of sample cost, separation of expenses by transaction and channel of distribution, and *target* profit objectives based on return on investment are illustrated in this chapter. A target profit mark-up based on conversion cost is recommended rather than percent of sales technique. Obsolescence and inventory cost are discussed along with the handling of interest on loans for cost calculation and target pricing. Illustrations include a chemical product cost sheet showing transaction cost, price breaks, and geographical zone price estimates.

Now, calculations have been completed. Chapter Nine will be devoted to pricing and pricing decisions; then, Chapter Ten will cover management information and control systems. In addition, international costing and pricing situations will be reviewed in these subsequent chapters.

CHAPTER NINE

Pricing for Growth and Profit

The correct pricing of products considers the market requirements, the competition, and the costs. This is essential for the attainment of management objectives for growth and return on investment.

On occasion, sales and market situations may seem to imply that pricing is the key to higher volume. In the long run, a successful business will be built on lower cost, better quality, and customer service.

The development of a marketing concept as an objective of management includes stimulating demand. One way of stimulating demand is through pricing. It would be excellent if all consumers could afford to purchase the best quality products. Yet, the ability to buy certain non-essential consumer products is usually related to the individual family's discretionary income.

Managers have a responsibility to provide products for the mass market consumer; and thereby stimulate real demand through products at lower price points.

It appears that prices are determined in the market-place by competitive conditions; however, by knowing the real costs and analyzing market prices, managers can select those products, markets, and channels of distribution which will generate the best financial results. The firm can then develop and allocate resources to these areas. This fact is particularly true for firms with complex product lines and diversified methods of selling and distribution.

The first step is to prepare data in a form in which it may be efficiently utilized. The detailed cost sheet (Figure 8-11) can be simplified into a Marketing Cost Sheet as illustrated in Figure 9-1. One of this type is helpful for sales, marketing, and management. This sheet displays the key cost elements required for pricing and evaluation of prices. It includes:

(a) Gross *Target* Selling Price—the price including terms and discounts which will generate the desired return on investment for a given normal volume and product mix.
(b) Net *Target* Selling Price—the gross target selling price less terms and discounts.
(c) Total Cost and Net Break-even Price—the net price which will recover all variable

and fixed costs for the given normal or standard volume, product mix, and depreciation based on replacement values.

(d) Total Variable Cost—the price which will recover all variable costs or out-of-pocket expenses.

(e) Contribution—the contribution to fixed cost and profits for sales at the *target* selling price.

(f) Profit—profit before taxes for sales at the target selling price (net selling price minus total cost).

(g) Percent Contribution—contribution as a percent of net target selling price.

(h) Percent Profit—gross profit before taxes as a percent of net target selling price.

(i) Contribution per Machine Hour—contribution per machine hour for the bottleneck cost center.

(j) Profit per Machine Hour—profit per machine hour for the bottleneck cost center.

In many manufacturing operations, there are one or two cost centers which account for substantial portions of costs or production potential. The plant must be balanced from a production standpoint around these "bottleneck" cost centers. In these situations, the contribution per machine hour may be a guide to the relative financial gains to be received from each of several products.

Selected specification data for the related cost calculations may be helpful. Blank columns are provided for updating as revisions to basic data are made or as there is an evaluation of actual prices.

Normally, costs and budgets are revised annually. Some products with a seasonal demand pattern may require semi-annual revisions. When significant changes occur, costs may be revised immediately.

Pricing Situations

A variety of pricing situations requiring variations in information, analysis and decisions face management. Prices for some products are difficult to change within a model, season, or other interval of time. Examples of these are automobiles and appliances. These semi-fixed price products are generally sold at the same price to all customers, except for quantity discounts; and may be more related to the industry competitive conditions than manufacturing cost.

Basic industrial prices for steels, chemicals, and similar items may be set by item. Yet, changes in prices are generally by product group. An example may be steel product groups including structural, plates, reinforcing, or other similar products.

For products where style, design, or color is important, product prices can sometimes be changed more frequently as cost considerations require. These may be considered variable prices.

Contract prices are those which are established for a given contract representative of a set quantity, time, and condition. These prices are usually fixed for the specific contract. They may vary from one contract to another, or the contract may be on a cost plus basis.

There are many products—steel, automobiles, and other basic items—where the price is set by market competition. In this situation, the calculated cost may not be a

Product No.   201   Name: All American

Channel of Distribution: Retail

Specification #501

Yarn Type: 3700 Denier, Nylon
Primary Back: 9.0 Oz. Jute
Latex: 26.0 Oz.
Secondary Back: 7.0 Oz. Jute
Carpet Type   Loop
Stitches/Inch   7.0
Gauge: 5/32"

Cost & Prices

                                        Target _____ _____

Gross Selling Price $3.70
Net Selling Price   3.48
Total Cost & Net Break-even Price   3.09
Total Variable Cost   2.45
Contribution   1.03
Profit   0.38

Contribution*   29.6 %
Profit*   10.9 %

Contribution/Tufting Machine Hour $229
Profit/Tufting Machine Hour   84

Special Conditions or Information: _____

_____

_____

* = Percent of Net Selling Price

FIGURE 9-1
MARKETING COST SHEET

significantly influencing factor in a manager's pricing decision. For industries where styling, design or other components can be revised—clothing, carpets, chemicals, and similar items—the calculated cost will be a significant consideration. Fact is, there are probably more products where costs are important factors than those which are established by the market. Regardless of the specific pricing situation, every manager must know his real cost for evaluating market prices, making decisions on investments, and determining those few areas to concentrate resources for the best financial results.

The difficulty with using market prices for setting product prices is determining the *real* market price. Too often, management can be misinformed on market prices when they are supplied by unreliable sources, both from within and outside the firm.

The orientation of this chapter is toward a manufacturer or business which adds value to the product, however, much of the logic is applicable to other pricing situations as well.

Volume Considerations

The basic considerations for volume are:

(a) adequate or excess demand with full capacity utilization.
(b) insufficient long-term demand with capacity idle, either for manufacturing or certain cost centers within manufacturing.
(c) insufficient short-term demand due to market or seasonal conditions.
(d) variations between full capacity utilization and idle capacity.

Where demand is adequate or in excess of capacity, the target selling price or a higher price should be the guide if the market demand is elastic over the range considered for an increase. The same logic applies when there is a shortage of materials or other resources. In situations with excess or idle capacity, the contribution is a better indicator.

The problem becomes challenging in determining the point between the target selling price and variable cost for a specific price. In the end, this will be an empirical judgment decision. Factors such as knowledge of competition, and knowledge of market conditions may determine the quoted market price. Other factors including the maintenance of stable employment and the cost of start-up and shutdown must be evaluated.

In theory, any contribution will be better than nothing at all. In fact, prices which generate less than one-half of the fixed expenses must be carefully considered to insure proper approval, and consistent pricing. Pricing guidelines, similar to those shown in Figure 9-2, should be developed as management's policy.

In markets such as bathing suits, construction materials, and consumer products, a seasonal pattern may be evident with idle capacity in some months. As an example, automotive parts suppliers' production is normally curtailed during model changeover. In this situation, it may be necessary to take certain contracts or enter into extensive sales promotions primarily to recover fixed cost and maintain continuous operations.

A contract analysis for Product Number 201 is shown in Figure 9-3. This contract analysis form shows the per unit and total contract financial results at target selling prices. In addition, columns are provided for sales and marketing functions to analyze specific actual expected prices.

Linear Programming

In many industries with multiple cost centers, complex product lines and variations in contribution between products, and linear programming (LP) offer managers a tool to determine a product mix to maximize profits.

POLICY AND JOB INSTRUCTIONS	Title: Pricing Guidelines

GENERAL POLICY STATEMENT

Though no formula is available which will reflect competitive and marketing conditions, these guidelines are the boundaries within which judgment decisions shall be made based on analytical information. The maximum price consistent with competitive marketing conditions will be quoted.

The Target Selling Price represents the pricing objective. This is the price which will generate the planned company profit, return on gross investment based on standard costs. It includes standard allowances for all variable costs, fixed costs, discounts, and profits.

(a) Where an exclusive marketing, material, technological, or other advantage exists, prices in excess of the target selling price will be quoted.

(b) Where competitive circumstances dictate, prices below the target selling price may be quoted with the proper approval.

(c) Quantity discounts and special prices may be quoted for large orders for stockkeeping items or special items.

(d) These guidelines apply to first quality pricing situations, only.

Pricing approval authorities are:

(a) Prices at or above the target selling prices may be established with the approval of the Vice-President of Sales & Marketing.

(b) Prices between the net break-even price and target selling price require the approval of the Vice-President of Sales & Marketing and the President.

(c) Prices below the net break-even price require the approval of the Executive Committee.

(d) Prices below the net break-even price which recover less than one-half of the fixed costs will not be quoted or established.

List prices quoted on identical or substantial similar items sold through both the retail and large volume channels of distribution will be consistent.

The Vice-President of Sales & Marketing is responsible for establishing, quoting, or otherwise determining prices and obtaining the proper approvals.

Issued By: Vice-Pres.Sales	Approved By: President	Superceded Date: None	Effective Date xx-xx-xx	No. 410.0

FIGURE 9-2
PRICING GUIDELINES

Product No. <u>201</u>   Name: <u>All American</u>

Channel of Distribution: Large Volume

                    <u>Specification #501</u>

                                    <u>Standard</u>   _____   _____

Number of Units   1   1,000

Gross Target Price $3.18 $3,180
Net Target Price   3.18   3,180

Total Cost & Net BE*Price $2.81 $2,810
Total Variable Cost   2.39   2,390

Contribution $0.77 $ 770
Profit   0.36   360

Special Conditions or Information: _____

_____

_____

_____

Quotation Approval: _____   _____
                            Date   Person

Results of Quotation: _____

_____

_____

*BE + Breakeven

FIGURE 9-3
CONTRACT ANALYSIS

Managers must insist that constraints on capacity in each center and market potential in each product are realistic. The contribution per unit employed in the model must reflect actuality over the range being considered. There is no need to work out an optimization problem for a market demand which cannot be achieved. Similarly, there is no reason to shift products from a higher cost to a low cost plant unless the higher cost plant is to be eliminated or curtailed.

In all linear programming problems, *contribution* to fixed cost and profit rather than profit alone must be the basis for comparisons of products. *Gross profit, total cost or marginal income simply will not give a valid solution when the volume or product mix changes significantly from the normal or standard conditions.* Gross profit is the contribution in excess of manufacturing costs, which includes fixed manufacturing expenses. Marginal income is the difference between sale revenue and variable cost.

Pricing Technological Advantages

Pricing decisions involving the consideration of technological advantages resulting from extensive Research & Development expenses require special costing and pricing considerations. Often, unusual, large, or non-recurring Research and Development expenses are incurred to develop a new product. Similarly, large advertising, sampling, or plant expenditures may be necessary. In some cases, an idle capacity in manufacturing facilities may result initially as market demand is expanding.

The write-off of these expenses may be programmed over a specified period of time, say five years; however, this write-off may be on an accelerated basis, rather than on a linear straight line basis.

The initial profit objective may be higher when the product is introduced and declining, as the technological advantage is reduced by competition. The final price will require management judgment based on a consideration of the importance of the technology, patent protection, competition, and market developments. A price must be established which will not slow the growth of the market. It is generally desirable to establish prices which will stimulate the development of the market at a rate consistent with the availability of capacity to produce. A lower price for higher sales is of no value unless the manufacturing capacity exists or can be provided.

Pricing in a Declining Market

Markets may decline in the short term for seasonal or other reasons, and these declines may require price changes. Most important is the long-term decline in demand resulting from changing methods of manufacture, and consumer needs. As an example, in the mid-1950's woven carpet commanded over ninety percent of the U. S. market. By the early 1970's, this type of carpet had declined to less than ten percent of the market. Other methods of manufacturing carpet have been developed and perfected. This decline resulted in surplus capacity as well as idle and obsolete equipment having no other potential utilization. In this and similar situations black and white television sets, piston engine airplanes, and others—for managers to maximize the financial results and postpone the market decline, the *contribution* of these products should be the guide for pricing. Prices lower than total cost would keep surplus facilities operating as they were consolidated or replaced by other types of manufacturing equipment.

Pricing and the Product Life Cycle

Most products have a life cycle in sales volume which starts at zero and expands as advertising or other factors create and stimulate demand. This cycle reaches a high point and, then, begins to decline as competition from other producers of the same or similar products enter the market. Figure 9-4 displays a product for which R & D effort began at point "A", plant start-up was initiated at point "B", and the product was available for shipment at point "C". The sale of automobile models, television set designs, and others follow this pattern with variations in the time frame and curve.

As sales volume increases, costs are reduced and volume expands, losses are eliminated and profits or contribution increases rapidly. As the technological, styling, or design advantages are achieved by competitors, market prices deteriorate which lowers the financial return.

Where a high degree of research and development result in patent protection, the volume and profit cycles are extended. In situations where there is little or no technological advantage, both sales and profits may be high on the "X" axis of Figure 9-4 and decline rapidly.

Effective managers must study and exploit the life cycles of products. Advertising, revisions in designs, and pricing strategies can expand the life cycles, increase financial results, and thwart competition. Once significant competition is in the market, pricing decisions based on contribution analysis may be the most effective.

Pricing Inter-Company Transfers

Normally, the objective of a plant or manufacturing operation is to maintain control of cost as determined by engineered standards. When this is accomplished with planned programs of costs reduction, manufacturing management frequently achieves its target.

Generally, those departments or operations which influence sales or revenues are the best for profit centers; whereas, those which are predominately concerned with cost are cost control centers. Inter-company transfers create paper work and administrative expense without adding to the value of the item. This additional expense must be evaluated versus anticipated gains from these transfers. With excessive transfers, there may be a loss in quality responsibility and material loss control. Once a product has been transferred, the question *What department caused the quality fault?* can lead to internal bickering and failure of all divisions to work together harmoniously.

Under this approach, the manufacturing unit is not considered a profit center. A market or business is responsible for generating profits. Transfers between divisions are priced at total standard cost. Though the manufacturing function is responsible for off-quality, the receiving division must absorb the price mark-down. Therefore, the cost for first quality merchandise is used, rather than the average cost. For Product Number 201, Figure 8-11, the value would be $2.440.

In situations where manufacturing points or divisions are profit centers, the transfer should include the price mark-up. Should Product Number 201 be transferred in-process after manufacturing through drying, the calculated transfer price would be:

Material (Excluding Packaging)	$1.811
Manufacturing	
Receiving & Tufting	0.113

Profit or Contribution

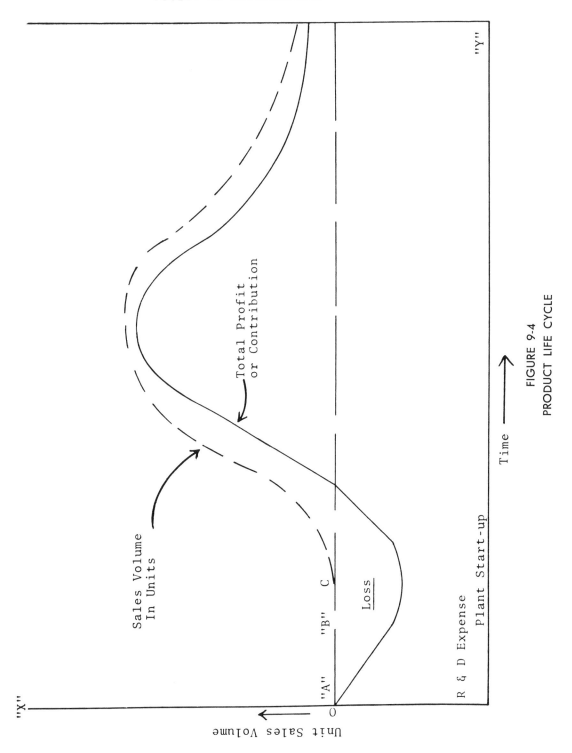

FIGURE 9-4
PRODUCT LIFE CYCLE

Dyeing	0.067
Drying	0.027
Total First Quality Manufacturing Costs	$2.018
Conversion Costs ($2.018 − $1.811)	0.207
Profit Mark-up (0.207 × 1.20)	0.248
Research & Development	0.048
Administration	0.076
Transfer Price ($2.018 + 0.248 + 0.048 + 0.076)	$2.390

The cost and pricing of the receiving division is complicated by the inclusion of profit. The transfer must include cost and profit as separate figures. The receiving division must use cost for pricing inventories. In order not to compound profit, the receiving division must reduce its profit mark-up target by the amount of profit assigned to the initial manufacturing division.

One way of handling inter-company prices is:

(a) *Entry on receiving plant records:*

Inventory—Direct Cost	XXXX	
Fixed Cost	XXXX	
Inter-plant Profit	XXXX	
Amount Due Receiving Plant		XXXX

(b) *Entry on shipping plant records:*

Inventory—Direct Cost		XXXX
Fixed Cost		XXXX
Inter-plant Profit		XXXX
Amount Due Shipping Plant	XXXX	

This method avoids having to wash out inter-company profits when statements are consolidated; it keeps inventories on a uniform basis; and it assists in avoiding the potential problem of overstating inventories. It also aids management in determining how much *paper* profit is being created by inter-company transfers. When this method is used, cost sheets must reflect the required direct cost, fixed cost, and inter-company profit.

Managers must insure that products transferred are costed and priced properly. Errors can distort financial results and lead to non-competitive market prices.

This is particularly important where percent of sales mark-ups are utilized for profit guides. If profit is transferred in the intra-transfer price; then, the mark-up in the receiving division for profit is added twice. This will lead to non-competitive market prices, and loss in confidence in the standard cost and target pricing system.

The physical location of a manufacturing process is not the determining factor as to whether it should be a profit center. If the operation performed is an integral part of the processing required for producing a useful product, it is a cost control center, not a profit center.

As an example, visualize the manufacturer of gears, where the blanks are milled and teeth are cut. Whether the gears are milled and cut in the same or separate physical plants is not a significant factor for determining cost control as compared with a profit center responsibility.

In cases where different divisions of management are responsible, control and communication conflicts can result. Certain manufacturers have a choice of performing some processes internally, or sending the product outside to commission or independent specialty firms.

As an example, assume a part is being made which requires painting. If the painting process is a separate, internal activity, transfers should be based on cost—not target selling price.

In the event that, for some reason, management wishes the painting operation to be a profit center, the transfer should not be at target selling price. A determination must be made of outside cost and priced on this basis. This gives managers a guide to the relative profitability of internal processing versus outside processing. The use of target selling prices leads to a guaranteed cost plus price and profit. Sometimes, inefficient production occurs which penalizes sales of the final product.

The percent contribution is sometimes considered as a basis for determining profits by division where products are transferred. This, like percent of sales, provides an excess profit distribution to the division which uses the most materials.

With cost variances and other considerations, a method of transferring products on standard cost is best. Where profit must be estimated, this component should be based on the conversion cost or value added. A percent of cost mark-up distorts real relationships.

Transferring products may be necessary for proper and efficient use of facilities. The transfer itself does not add value to the product. Managers must not spend a great deal of time developing or refereeing inter-divisional disputes or allowing these to cause friction within the organization.

International Pricing

First, managers must determine whether the objective in foreign markets is one of export or international marketing. Export, on occasions, may be a means of getting rid of a temporary over-supply.

If, on the other hand, the target is to market one's products over the long run in a foreign market, a different approach is required. In determining a plan for international marketing, managers may wish to ask the following questions:

1. What is the potential volume of the market, the type of competition, and related factors?
2. At what prices are products in the market serving a similar need as those proposed to be marketed?
3. Are the products available in the foreign market of the same technical quality?

4. What profit, or contribution to gross profit can be expected considering taxes, duties, transport, agent fees and other cost?
5. Is there a sector of the foreign market which would be willing to pay a higher price for a better quality product? If so, how high a price?

These, and many other factors require evaluation.

International sales can provide a very effective way of increasing volume. These sales serve as a basis for building a market in other countries and subsequently implementing manufacturing operations.

Often, sales in countries other than the home market have different seasonal and cyclical relationships than domestic markets. An international market may be expanding at a time concurrent with a decline in the home market, and this leads to a use of capacity which may be otherwise temporarily idle.

International markets also provide a way of making better use of Research and Development expenses. Often, doing business in other countries provides exposure to new technology, marketing methods, or management ideas which can be used at home.

The first step in pricing for a foreign market is to learn the laws relative to taxes and duties. Some countries take a protective viewpoint, and they will not permit products to be sold below the firm's home market price. This is done to prevent the dumping of excess capacity.

Generally, international cost calculations follow those for large volume sales in the home market. Domestic advertising is not included. Each expense must be analyzed— samples, administrative accounts, and others—to determine if it is related to the foreign sales.

Some firms have considered foreign sales (exports) as plus business. This has led to deleting Research and Development expenses from export costs and lowering the profit requirements. In the long run, these sales must recover all applicable costs and generate a return on the investment consistent with management's objective.

The cost for packaging materials must be changed to reflect the higher cost of export packaging. Insurance and handling fees must be added. Freight, as determined by the terms of sales, must be included either to the domestic port or foreign port.

Where foreign agents or distributors are involved, a commission payment may be included. Often, the terms of payment and the time the inventory is in the pipeline is significantly longer. This results in a higher investment and larger profit mark-up requirement than the home market, even though the costs may be lower.

Should the terms of payment include accepting foreign currency, a gain or loss of foreign exchange must be evaluated. First, it is necessary to determine whether the foreign currency can be exchanged or if there is a probability of a revision in the rate of exchange.

Local taxes must be studied to determine whether profits on sales to another country are taxable. Many countries have manufacturers or turnover taxes which are applicable, possibly indirectly, to the imports.

Managers must carefully prepare the costs, terms, and conditions of sales to achieve a desired return on foreign sales, and plan international marketing programs.

An example of an export pricing for Product Number 201 may be:

Target Selling Price (Large Volume)	$3.175
Adjustment for Packaging Cost	+0.035
Adjustment for Terms	+0.062
Freight to the Port	+0.100
Export Handling & Fees	+0.015
Adjustment for Selling & Marketing Expense	−0.060
Agent Fees & Commissions	+ 0.125
Total Export Target Selling Price FOB Savannah, Georgia	$3.452

From these data, management must then determine the actual price, contract terms and conditions. Most frequently where foreign sales are continuous and represent an important part of the firm's business, specific detail cost sheets must be prepared in a manner similar to the domestic market.

For long-run sales in international markets, the products must be priced in local currency, delivered and serviced from a local point. This will require manufacturing distribution facilities in the particular country or trade block. The alternative will be for the firm to completely handle the shipment and expenses to the point of distribution in the foreign market.

Should the sales be a leader into the foreign market for future operations into that country or trade group, it may be necessary to simulate a manufacturing, marketing and distribution organization in the other country. This will require preparing a cost and business plan similar to the home market. A key factor in the foreign market business plan will be the normal volume operations. In some countries, outside the U.S.A., more holidays and vacations are allowed. In France, for instance, 45 or 46 weeks per year may be the normal plant operation. This reduced operation and longer idle production capacity contributes significantly to higher cost and profit mark-ups. A similar situation may exist on the number of shifts operated per day.

Simulating operations in Canada, the costing, and pricing of Product Number 201, would result in a cost and target selling price calculation as shown in Figure 9-5. A comparison to U.S. costs is included.

A number of factors cause the costs to be higher in Canada rather than the United States. First, the value or exchange rate of the currency is a factor. Next, Canada is a country geographically larger than the United States. Yet, the population is approximately ten percent of that in the U.S. This distribution over a broad expanse of geography with lower demand results in a substantially higher distribution cost for like items.

Canadian manufacturers must make the same range of products for the smaller market as would be required for the larger U.S. market. This results in shorter unit runs in manufacturing operations, larger relative inventories, and a higher relationship of obsolescence or discontinued items. Frequently, many customers of manufacturers are not capable of financing their operations. This results in larger and longer accounts receivable with the manufacturer, in effect, financing the customer's operation.

Product No. <u>201</u>   Name: <u>All American</u>

Specification #501

	U. S. $	Canadian $
		Min. Max.
Material	$2.14	$2.30 / 2.40
Labor	0.10	.20 / .30
Variable Manufacturing Expense	0.08	.15 / .25
Fixed Manufacturing Expense	<u>0.12</u>	<u>.15 / .20</u>
Sub-Total	$2.44	$2.80 / 3.15
Off-Quality & Claims	<u>0.07</u>	<u>.10 / .10</u>
Sub-Total	$2.51	$2.90 / 3.25
Distribution, Selling, R & D, and Administration	<u>0.59</u>	<u>.50</u>	<u>.90</u>
Total Cost	$3.10	$3.40	4.15
Profit	<u>0.38</u>	<u>.40</u>	<u>.55</u>
Net Target Price	$3.48	$3.80	4.70

$4.25

Most Likely

FIGURE 9-5

UNITED STATES COST COMPARED TO CANADIAN COST

In Canada, a manufacturer's tax is added. This tax, when compounded through the distribution system, requires a substantially higher retail price in Canada for a like product in the U.S.A. This higher retail price, coupled with a lower discretionary income of the average Canadian family, depresses demand and growth levels below those experienced in the U.S. market.

International pricing must be based on the firm's long-range policy. It is suspect to enter an export market with low prices to utilize excess capacity; then, decide to increase prices and methods of distribution drastically upon implementation of manufacturing in that country.

Managers must allocate sufficient resources including personnel with language capability, funds for legal studies, market research, tax analysis, and others to thoroughly understand export markets for these to contribute to effective financial results. Increased sales volume alone is not sufficient justification for export sales. Other texts and studies should be consulted for a complete evaluation of the potential of existing foreign operations.

Quantity Discounts

Quantity discounts are an effective way of increasing sales dollars, and most important, dollar value per shipment. The first step is to evaluate all costs associated with transactions—order processing, credit checking, invoicing, accounts receivable, data processing, shipping, and others. In some cases where orders are taken in person, the sales costs per call must be included.

The study and determination of transaction costs is especially important for firms with low dollar values per invoice of, say less than, $500 per invoice. Even with the most efficient system designed, it simply may not be possible to achieve the desired growth of the firm in this range unless the dollar value per shipment is increased.

Analyzing the cost changes from a seller's point of view is one aspect of the quantity price. From the buyer standpoint, higher inventory costs may result. The buyer should have less ordering expense plus the gain from the lower price of the larger quantities.

In all cases, quantity discounts must be related to costs. The important factor is the size of shipments and number of points to be shipped.

Often, costs are created, rather than profits increased, by one large contract which requires shipping and billing of small quantities to multiple outlets. Quantity pricing normally refers to quantity shipped and billed to one source.

An example of quantity pricing is shown in Figure 9-6. The first substantial price break is the quantity which changes the freight rate from minimum to less than truck load (LTL). The next significant break is the quantity which will generate a truck load freight rate.

Managers must be careful to consider the laws and other legal factors related to quantity prices in making decisions. Variable items, such as freight, are generally valid. The inclusion of fixed cost elements may be suspect.

	One Unit	Three Units	Five Units	Truck Load Quantity
Manufacturing Costs	$12.00	$12.00	$12.00	$12.00
Fixed Expenses:				
Transaction Costs/Case	3.00	1.00	0.60	0.05
Other	6.00	6.00	6.00	4.50
Profit	2.00	2.00	2.00	2.00
Target Selling Price	$23.00	$21.00	$20.60	$18.55
Freight to Warehouse (TL)	2.00	2.00	2.00	-
Warehouse to Customer (Minimum, & LTL or TL)	4.50	3.75	3.25	2.75
Total Selling Price Delivered	$29.50	$26.75	$25.85	$21.30
Quantity Price Discount Per Case	-	$ 2.75	$ 3.65	$ 8.20

FIGURE 9-6

CALCULATION OF QUANTITY PRICE

Price Control

Equally or more important as calculation of target prices is the control of prices. In many situations, individual salesmen do not have the authority to change a price. Yet, management must know how much the prices vary from the target required for the objective return on investment.

The cost sheet calculation estimates a target selling price for first quality goods. A standard price must be set, *often based on market conditions,* for off-quality and discontinued or obsolete items.

The off-quality or obsolescence loss can be budgeted based on expected quantity and prices. Other departments may be responsible for quantity variances—excess off-quality or excess inventory of discontinued items. Sales and Marketing is responsible for the price variance from the standard price for these items.

An example of a Price Control Statement is shown in Figure 9-7. This separates sales by product, quality, and channel of distribution.

PRODUCT NUMBER	PRODUCT NAME	SALES VOLUME UNITS	NET TARGET PRICE (PER UNIT)	NET TARGET DOLLAR (TOTAL)	ACTUAL PRICE (PER UNIT)	NET ACTUAL DOLLAR (TOTAL)	PRICE VARIANCE GAIN (LOSS)	PRICE RATIO (CCL.7 COL.5)	CHANNEL OF DISTRIBUTION
FIRST QUALITY PRODUCT									
201	ALL AMERICAN	100,000	$3,475	$347,500	$3,450	$345,000	($2,500)	0,992	RETAIL
		50,000	3,127	156,350	3,000	150,000	($6,350)	0,959	LARGE VOLUME
OFF-QUALITY PRODUCT									
201	ALL AMERICAN	10,000	$2,500	$ 25,000	$2,600	$ 26,000	$1,000	1,040	ALL
OBSOLETE OR DISCONTINUED PRODUCTS									
110		5,000	$2,000	$ 10,000	$1,500	$ 7,500	($2,500)	0,750	ALL

FIGURE 9-7
PRICE CONTROL STATEMENT

The price ratio is an indicator of the relationship of the actual price to the target price, or:

$$\text{Price Ratio} = \frac{\text{Actual Price}}{\text{Target Price}}$$

A ratio of 1.000 means that the actual price was identical to the target price. These ratios can be charted or otherwise compared in time series to show the changes in price trends by product, by customer, or other meaningful category.

Analysis of the type shown in Figure 9-7 can be prepared by customer, division, sales territory or other breakdown as may be required. Where off-quality is classified by cause, price variances by degree of severity or off-quality defect may be determined.

The total price variance can be transferred to the Management Control Statement, Chapter 10, as an explanation of variation in the actual profit from the target profit objective of the business.

Pricing decisions are some of the most important decisions made by managers. It would be helpful if these could be reduced to a set of rules. This is not the case. *Effective pricing decisions will be based on an analytical approach utilizing management judgment as the markets, the competition, and the costs continually change.*

SUMMARY

The correct pricing of products considers the market requirements, the competition, and the costs. This is essential for the attainment of management objectives for growth and return on investment.

It often appears that prices are established in the marketplace and this is true for many products. By knowing the real cost and by analyzing market prices, managers can select those products, markets, or channels of distribution which will generate the best financial results.

In this chapter, a simplified marketing cost sheet is developed, and various pricing and volume situations are examined. A policy on pricing is illustrated. Special attention is given to contract analysis, pricing technological advantages, declining market pricing, and inter-company transfers.

A special section explains the potential problems and factors relating to foreign pricing and international marketing. An example of the difference between the higher cost for manufacturing and distribution in Canada is illustrated. Managers must carefully prepare the costs, terms, and conditions of sales to achieve a desired return on foreign sales.

Quantity discounts are an effective way of increasing sales dollars per transaction. Yet, costs are created, rather than profits increased, by one large contract which requires shipping and billing of small quantities to multiple outlets. Quantity pricing normally refers to quantity shipped and billed to one source. Managers must be careful to comply with current laws relative to quantity or other pricing differentiation of similar products.

Equally as important as establishing the proper price is the control of prices. Price Control Statements of variances and price ratios are illustrated.

Pricing decisions are some of the most important decisions made by management. It would be helpful if these could be based on established formulas. Effective pricing decisions require judgment considering the market, the competition, and the costs as these continue to change.

The following chapter will cover the use of information for management control, decisions, and actions.

CHAPTER TEN

Management Information for Control, Decisions, and Actions

The utilization of data and information for decisions and actions as conditions change is the basis for effective management and financial results. Given, then, that the business plan has been developed, how can a manager effectively use this information?

Basically the control of a business enterprise has three levels. These are:

1. Line or shift supervisor level.
2. Department or plant manager level.
3. Management or executive level.

Management Control Statement

Control statements for the first two levels have been considered earlier. A typical management control statement for the executive level is shown in Figure 10-1. From this statement, management can get an overview of the business enterprise. This example is for a quarterly time interval. Monthly statements are necessary for proper control.

The statement is designed to help managers *ask the right question,* and to display changes in trends. It is not designed to analyze the reasons for changes in every case.

A forecast for the current year and a comparison of the current year's actual results to last year's performance are displayed. The forecast is an essential element of the management control statements. It requires all executives to evaluate objectives and performance, and it gives information on predicted future results. This permits management to take action to change the course of events should the forecasted results not be satisfactory.

A Management Control Statement of this type is for internal management utilization only. For external profit reporting to stockholders and for tax statements, these

183

statements must be adjusted for any variances which do not conform to accepted required practice. For this example, the only difference would be depreciation. It is based on replacement values, rather than book values. This standard depreciation must be adjusted for external reporting to book values.

Sometimes, statements relate only to real historical data from actual situations; and although this is important, management control is concerned with forecasts and possible future results as well as information on past performance. The key for management is the comparison of target or objective profit with actual profit considering the information as to why this target was or was not achieved. As an example, the results for the first quarter of the current year in Figure 10-1 are:

Actual Gross Profit	$1,000,000	
Target Profit	550,000	
Variances:		
Price—First Quality	240,000	Gain
Off-Quality	10,000	Gain
Claim & Returns	(20,000)	Loss
Obsolete Merchandise	(30,000)	Loss
Materials Usage	20,000	Gain
Materials Price	(40,000)	Loss
Labor	10,000	Gain
Variable Manufacturing Expenses	20,000	Gain
Fixed Expenses	(10,000)	Loss
Volume & Product Mix	250,000	Gain
Total Variances	$ 450,000	Gain

From these variances, it can be determined:

(a) Actual selling prices were in excess of the target selling prices which increased profits by $240,000. Subsidiary reports should indicate price variances for each product, first quality products, off-quality products, and obsolete products. Sales & Marketing management is responsible for all price variances.

(b) The loss on sales and production of off-quality merchandise was less than standard and resulted in a $10,000 gain. This is only a quantity variance which is a manufacturing responsibility.

(c) Claims and return allowances including policy adjustments exceeded standard by ($20,000).

(d) The sale of inventory mark-down of discontinued or obsolete products was ($30,-000) in excess of the standard allowed. This item, too, is a quantity variance. This variance could be the responsibility of sales and marketing, product development, or distribution depending on whether it was a result of faulty planning, forecasting, or production control.

(e) Materials usage, a manufacturing responsibility has a gain of $20,000.

(f) Materials price loss of ($40,000) is a purchasing responsibility.

(g) Labor, which would be documented by department and job title on other reports gained $10,000.

Quarter Ending: $000

Left section — Quarter Ending ($000), Actuals by quarter and Last Year

Quarter Ending	Actual	Actual	Actual	Actual	Year Actual
Gross Sales	$5,000	$4,000	$6,000	$8,000	$23,000
Less: Terms	250	200	300	400	1,150
Net Sales	4,750	3,800	5,700	7,600	21,850
Variable Cost	$3,850	$3,100	$4,500	$5,900	$17,350
Contribution	900	700	1,200	1,700	4,500
Per Cent	19%	18%	21%	22%	21%
Fixed Cost	$650	$600	$600	$700	$2,550
Profit	250	100	600	1,000	1,950
Less: Provision for Taxes	125	50	300	500	975
Net Profit	$125	$50	$300	$500	$975
Depreciation	100	100	100	100	400
Cash Flow	225	150	400	600	1,375
Variance	($300)	($400) ($50)		$150	($600)
Return on Standard Investment	9.5%	3.8%	22.9%	38.0%	18.6%
Return on Actual Investment	11.2%	4.6%	27.9%	45.6%	22.4%
Net Profit - % of Net Sales	2.6%	1.3%	5.3%	6.6%	4.5%

Fixed Cost detail: Manufacturing, Distribution, Sales Marketing, Research, Administration

Variance detail lines: Price - 1st Quality, Off Quality, Obsolescence, Claims/Returns, Materials Usage, Materials Price, Labor, Variable Manufacturing, Fixed Manufacturing, Fixed Distribution, Fixed Sales/Marketing, Fixed Research, Fixed Administration, Volume, Product Mix, Target Profit

Middle section — This Yr Actual, Forecast columns, Current Year Forecast

Line	This Yr Actual	Forecast	Forecast	Forecast	Current Year Forecast
Gross Sales	$7,000	$5,000	$7,000	$8,000	$27,000
Less: Terms	350	250	350	400	1,350
Net Sales	6,650	4,750	6,650	7,600	25,650
Variable Cost	$5,000	$3,600	$5,000	$5,900	$19,500
Contribution	1,650	1,150	1,650	1,700	6,150
Per Cent	25%	24%	25%	22%	24%
Fixed Cost	$650	$600	$600	$700	$2,550
Profit	1,000	550	1,050	1,000	3,600
Less: Provision for Taxes	500	275	525	500	1,800
Net Profit	$500	$275	$525	$500	$1,800
Depreciation	100	100	100	100	400
Cash Flow	600	375	625	600	2,200
Variance	$450	$50	$400	$150	$1,050
Return on Standard Investment	38.0%	21.0%	40.0%	38.0%	34.3%
Return on Actual Investment	45.6%	25.4%	48.0%	45.6%	41.1%
Net Profit - % of Net Sales	7.5%	5.8%	7.9%	6.6%	7.0%

Right section — This Quarter and Year-To-Date

Line	This Quarter Forecast	This Quarter Actual	This Quarter Variance	YTD Last M	YTD This Yr	YTD Variance
Gross Sales	$6,000	$7,000	$1,000	$5,000	$7,000	$2,000
Less: Terms	300	350	50	250	350	100
Net Sales	5,700	6,650	950	4,750	6,650	1,900
Variable Cost	$4,300	$5,000	$700	$3,850	$5,000	$1,150
Contribution	1,200	1,650	450	900	1,650	750
Per Cent	21%	25%	4%	19%	25%	6%
Fixed Cost	$640	$650	($10)	$650	$650	$-
Profit	560	1,000	440	250	1,000	750
Less: Provision for Taxes	280	500	220	125	500	375
Net Profit	$280	$500	$220	$125	$500	$375
Depreciation	100	100	-	100	225	100
Cash Flow	380	600	220	225	600	375
Variance	$10	$450	$440	($300)	$450	$750
Return on Standard Investment	21.2%	38.0%	16.8%	9.5%	38.0%	28.5%
Return on Actual Investment	25.6%	45.6%	20.0%	11.2%	45.6%	34.4%
Net Profit - % of Net Sales	4.9%	7.5%	2.6%	2.6%	7.5%	4.9%

FIGURE 10-1

MANAGEMENT CONTROL STATEMENT

(h) Variable manufacturing expense gain of $20,000 should tie into other control reports by department and plant.

(i) Fixed expenses indicate a loss of $10,000. A subsidiary report of budgets would detail each department and responsibility by account to verify this variance.

(j) Volume and product mix are accounts which requires special analysis to explain. In this example, a forecasted contribution rate of 21 percent and a $950,000 net sales volume variance gain, approximately $200,000 of the profit variance is the result of sales volume. The amount of $50,000 is due to selling the product mix with a better contribution rate.

The total package of management information would include the management control statement, plus key cost, quality, budget and sales analysis information. In addition, a balance sheet detailing assets, liabilities, and other financial statistics would be included for management's consideration.

Cash Flow

An important financial guide for cash forecasting is the cash flow. Cash flow is the money available to the firm for payment of loans, capital expenditures, and other cash requirements.

$$\text{Cash Flow} = \text{Depreciation} + \text{Net Profit After Tax}$$

A source and application of funds analysis from the management control statements may be as indicated in Figure 10-2. From this analysis management can estimate the amount of money available for expansion, acquisitions, or investments. Source and application of funds forecasts are particularly useful for firms operating on a heavy debt structure, or in times of poor financial performance, or in regard to large capital expenditures. Management must have an accurate monthly, sometimes weekly, and possibly daily funds forecast to effectively utilize the financial resources of the firm.

To obtain the change in inventory requirements for cash, it is necessary to have a forecast of shipments and a production plan. The difference between the sales or shipments forecast and the production plan is the expected change in inventory. The net result is the change in cash needs or availability of cash due to inventory changes.

If the firm is privately held, the real indicator of performance may be cash flow, rather than profits. With a privately held firm, the objective may be to increase assets at the expense of profits. With a publicly held firm, the profit performance may be more important to investors and stockholders.

Sales and Profit Forecasting

Given the normal volume, or a specific sales forecast by item, a sales and profit forecast as illustrated in Figure 10-3 can be prepared. By multiplying the individual

	Quarter Ending - $000			
	3/31 Actual	6/30 Forecast	9/30 Forecast	12/31 Forecast
Source of Funds				
Net Profits	$ 600	$ 375	$ 625	$ 600
Depreciation	100	100	100	100
Beginning Balance	400	600	925	1,400
Total Funds Available	$1,100	$1,075	$1,650	$2,100
Application of Funds				
Capital Expenditures	$ 100	$ 50	$ 200	$ 75
Inventory Change	+ 100	+ 300	- 250	- 150
Accounts Receivable Change	+ 300	- 200	+ 300	+ 500
Balance	$ 600	$ 925	$1,400	$1,675

FIGURE 10-2
SOURCE AND APPLICATION OF FUNDS

values times the quantity forecasted for each item, the total forecast can be accumulated.

The simulated firm for the normal volume and product mix will have gross sales of $28,350,000 for 6,500,000 square yards of carpet. Net sales of $26,150,000 will contribute $6,800,000 after variable costs of $19,350,000. Fixed costs of $4,250,000 leaves a profit before tax of $2,550,000.

A contribution rate of 26 percent means that each dollar of net sales will contribute $0.26 to fixed cost and profit.

Sales and profit forecasts of this type can be calculated for divisions, other business units, or product mixes.

Breakeven Point Calculation

Based on the normal volume of sales and profit forecast, the breakeven point can be plotted or calculated. This is the point in sales dollars or units for the given product mix at which fixed costs have been recovered and profits begin to accrue. This one is on an annual basis. Similar points can be calculated for monthly or other financial reporting periods.

A breakeven point is plotted in Figure 10-4. First, plot the fixed cost line, $4,250,-000. Next, plot the total cost point for 6,500,000 units and draw the total costs line.

```
                        DATE: XX-XX-XX
          DIVISION: HOME FURNISHINGS              PLANT: ATLANTA


          SQUARE YARDS (000)                            6,500


          TARGET SALES                              $28,350

          LESS:  TERMS                                1,150

                 OBSOLESCENCE                           385

                 CLAIMS/RETURNS                         665

          NET SALES                                 $26,150


          VARIABLE COST:

                 MATERIALS                         $17,359
                 LABOR                               1,050
                 LABOR EXPENSE                         225
                 MANUFACTURING                         378
                 DISTRIBUTION                          338

          SUB-TOTAL:  VARIABLE COST               $19,350


          CONTRIBUTION                            $ 6,800

          CONTRIBUTION RATE                            26%

          FIXED COST:

                 MANUFACTURING                   $    790
                 DISTRIBUTION                          468
                 RESEARCH + DEVELOPMENT                363
                 SALES + MARKETING                   1,718
                 ADMINISTRATION                        911

          SUB-TOTAL:  FIXED COST                  $ 4,250


          PROFIT BEFORE TAXES                     $ 2,550

          PROVISION FOR TAXES                     $ 1,275

          PROFIT AFTER TAXES                      $ 1,275

          RETURN ON GROSS INVESTMENT                  12.5%
```

FIGURE 10-3

SALES AND PROFIT FORECAST

$$
\begin{aligned}
\text{Total Cost Point} &= \text{Variable Cost} + \text{Fixed Cost} \\
&= \$19{,}350{,}000 \;+\; \$4{,}250{,}000 \\
&= \$23{,}600{,}000
\end{aligned}
$$

Then, plot the net sales point, $26,150,000 for the related sales units, and draw the sales line from the [0,0] coordinates. This assumes a linear relationship in both cases.

The point where the sales and cost lines cross is the breakeven point, for the given conditions. By extending a line from this point to the vertical scale, the breakeven

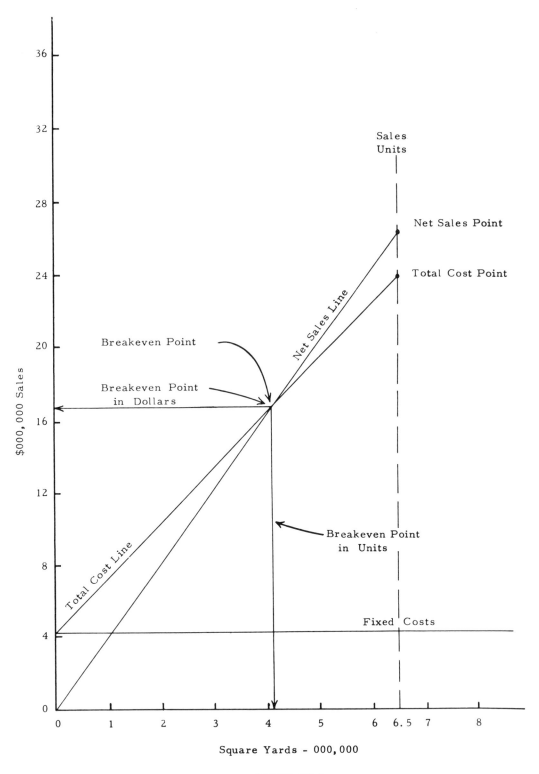

FIGURE 10-4
BREAKEVEN CHART

point in dollars can be estimated. Dropping a line down from the point to the horizontal scale gives the break-even point in units. These two points can be calculated.

$$\text{Break-even Point In Dollars} = \frac{\text{Total Fixed Cost}}{\text{Contribution Rate}}$$

$$= \frac{\$4,250,000}{\$0.26}$$

$$= \$16,346,000$$

$$\text{Break-even Point in Units} = \frac{\text{Break-even Point in Dollars}}{\text{Net Sales Price per unit}}$$

$$\text{Net Sales Price per Unit} = \frac{\text{Total Net Sales Dollars}}{\text{Total Units}}$$

$$= \frac{\$26,150,000}{6,500,000}$$

$$= \$4.023$$

$$\begin{array}{l}\text{Break-even Point in Units} \\ \text{for the Normal Product Mix}\end{array} = \frac{\$16,346,000}{\$4.023}$$

$$= 4,063,000$$

It is important to note that the breakeven point in units is for the given normal volume product mix. Variations in product mix reduce or make meaningless a break-even point in units.

Forecasting Reduced Operations

From data of this type, managers can obtain information to guide decisions and actions in scheduling operations. A question may be, "What would be the effect of reducing operations to four days, or 96 hours per week instead of the normal 120 hours?"

$$\begin{array}{l}\textit{Sales Volume} \\ \text{4 Days per Week} \\ \text{Operation}\end{array} = \$26,150,000 \times \frac{\text{4 Days}}{\text{5 Days}}$$

$$= \$20,920,000$$

With a contribution rate of 26 percent, the contribution would be:

$$\text{Contribution} = \$20,920,000 \times 0.26$$

$$= \$ 5,439,000$$

The forecasted Profit for four-day operations is:

$$\text{Profit} = \text{Contribution} - \text{Fixed Costs}$$

$$= \$ 5,439,000 - \$4,250,000$$

$$= \$ 1,189,000$$

When real conditions change significantly, the profit calculations are invalid. It is in these cases that contribution analysis, similar to the type just illustrated, is the valid indicator of financial results for the short term.

The fact that in certain cases profit calculations may not be correct does not invalidate the use of profit estimates. Managers must recognize when any parameter of volume, product mix, or other changes occur, they must respond accordingly.

The key is "true and important" differences. Everything in a business situation is variable and in error to a certain extent. The only "true and important" error is one which would significantly affect the financial performance.

The analysis presented herein assumes that labor cost can be reduced for the short term. Often, labor must be maintained on a reasonable schedule. This requires payments for reduced schedules. Labor, under these conditions, approaches a fixed cost. In the years ahead, managers must plan to manage and operate businesses with labor as a fixed expense for short-term decisions.

Forecasting Increased Operations

Another management question which frequently arises is, "What would be the financial results of increasing operations from five to six days per week?" First, an analysis must be made of the variances which will change as a result of the increase in volume. These are:

1. Labor cost due to increased operation and overtime.
2. Variable labor expenses of social security and possibly others. Holiday pay and certain of these expenses will not change.

The results, then, would be a forecast as shown in Figure 10-5. Comparing five and six days operations, this analysis assumes that the additional output is being shipped for end use consumption. Should it be going into inventory, an inventory carrying cost would have to be added to the costs shown in this estimate.

A similar type of analysis would indicate the result of increasing production from two to three shifts for the entire firm. On occasions, it is necessary to estimate the cost of operating a particular cost center for an additional shift in order to eliminate a bottleneck in production. An example of two-shift versus three-shift operation of the simulated firm Dyeing Department is shown in Figure 10-6. Labor cost increases are for the third shift including shift premium plus additional service department labor.

The costs per square yard for Product Number 201 are:

	Two Shift	Three Shift
Machine Hours/100 SY	0.60	0.58
Cost per Square Yard:		
Labor	$0.020	$0.018
Variable	0.029	0.028
Fixed	0.018	0.011
Total	$0.067	$0.057

```
                          DATE: XX-XX-XX
DIVISION: HOME FURNISHINGS                    PLANT: ATLANTA

                              FIVE DAY        SIX DAY
                              OPERATION       OPERATION
    SQUARE  YARDS               6,500           7,800

    TARGET SALES              $28,350         $34,020
    LESS'  TERMS                1,150           1,380
           OBSOLESCENCE           385             462
           CLAIMS/RETURNS         665             798

    NET SALES                 $26,150         $31,380

    VARIABLE COST:

           MATERIALS          $17,359         $20,830
           LABOR                1,050           1,365
           LABOR EXPENSE          225             270
           MANUFACTURING          378             454
           DISTRIBUTION           338             406

    SUB-TOTAL:   VARIABLE COST $19,350         $23,325

    CONTRIBUTION              $ 6,800         $ 8,055

    CONTRIBUTION RATE             26%             26%

    FIXED COST:

           MANUFACTURING      $    790         $    790
           DISTRIBUTION            468             468
           RESEARCH + DEVELOPMENT  363             363
           SALES + MARKETING     1,718           1,718
           ADMINISTRATION         911             911

    SUB-TOTAL:   FIXED COST   $ 4,250         $ 4,250

    PROFIT BEFORE TAXES       $ 2,550         $ 3,805

    PROVISION FOR TAXES  (50%) $ 1,275         $ 1,903

    PROFIT AFTER TAXES        $ 1,275         $ 1,902
```

FIGURE 10-5

SALES AND PROFIT FORECAST—INCREASED OPERATIONS

The lower machine hours (higher production per machine hour) for a three shift operaton is due to less start-up and shutdown loss. In some situations, fatigue losses result from three-shift operation. These may be offset by a reduction in start-up and shutdown losses. Two shift operation was calculated originally in Figure 6-1.

In many cases, the expansion from two to three shifts may require changes in *fixed* cost. This is particularly true where shift supervisors are on salary rather than on an hourly payroll.

Sales Price Change

Frequently, it appears to managers that a lower sales price will greatly increase sales and profits. The question is, "What additional volume is required to justify a four percent reduction in selling prices?"

Complete Cost Center Worksheet
Dyeing Department

(1)(2)(3)	(4) Labor Cost → Methods & Standard Summary	Service Dept.	(7) Variable Cost/Week Labor Benefits	(9) Mfg. Expense	(10) Fixed Mfg. Expense	(12) Total Cost
<u>One Shift Operation</u>						
Cost/Week	$2400	$980	$710	$4000	$2844	$10734
Number of Machines	12					
Operating Hours 2 Shifts, 40 Hours each	X 80					
Total Machine Hours	= 960	960	960	960	960	960
Cost Per Machine Hour	$2.50	$0.81 } $3.31	$0.74 $4.17 } $4.91		$2.97	$11.18
<u>Two Shift Operation</u>						
Cost Per Week	$3660	$920	$1065	$6000	$2844	$14477
Number of Machines	12					
Operating Hours 3 Shifts, 40 Hours each	120					
Total Machine Hours	1440	1440	1440	1440	1440	1440
Cost Per Machine Hour	$2.54	$0.64 } $3.18	$0.74 $4.16 } $4.90		$1.78	$10.06

FIGURE 10-6

COMPLETE COST CENTER WORKSHEET—
TWO-SHIFT VERSUS THREE-SHIFT OPERATION

```
                          DATE: XX-XX-XX
            DIVISION: HOME FURNISHINGS           PLANT: ATLANTA

            SQUARE YARDS (000)                              6,175


            NET SALES                                   $23,850


            VARIABLE COST:

                    MATERIALS                       $16,821
                    LABOR                             1,017
                    LABOR EXPENSE                       218
                    MANUFACTURING                       366
                    DISTRIBUTION                        328

            SUB-TOTAL:  VARIABLE COST              $18,750


            CONTRIBUTION                            $ 5,100

            CONTRIBUTION RATE                          21.4%


            FIXED COST:

                    MANUFACTURING                   $    890
                    DISTRIBUTION                          468
                    RESEARCH + DEVELOPMENT                363
                    SALES + MARKETING                  1,918
                    ADMINISTRATION                     1,011

            SUB-TOTAL:  FIXED COST                  $ 4,650


            PROFIT BEFORE TAXES                     $    450


            PROVISION FOR TAXES (50%)               $    225


            PROFIT AFTER TAXES                      $    225
```

FIGURE 10-7

SALES AND PROFIT FORECAST—A BUSINESS SITUATION

For the simulated firm sales and profit forecast, the contribution rate, as shown in Figure 10-3, was 26 percent. A four percent reduction would reduce this to 22 percent. The sales volume required to equal the $6,800,000 would be:

$$\text{Sales Volume Required} = \frac{\text{Contribution}}{\text{Contribution Rate}}$$
$$= \frac{\$6,800,000}{0.22}$$
$$= \$30,910,000$$

A dollar volume increase in net sales from $26,150,000 to $30,910,000 or approximately 18 percent is required to offset a four percent price reduction.

Managers must insist that specific targets are established and achieved by price reductions to obtain desired sales and profits. Long-run business success will result from superior quality, lower costs, and better service. Price reductions are the easy way, and sometimes an indication of weakness in other areas.

A Business Situation

Most business enterprises can survive one problem at a time. These may include higher labor cost, lower sales volume, or other crises.

The enthusiasm for expansion when sales and profits are high can cloud management's perspective. An expansion generally results in large increase in sales volume and profit forecast. Effective managers must consider the alternatives and the probabilities associated with possible outcomes of business environments.

As an example, the simulated firm is forecasting an expansion which will require certain buildings and equipment additions. Machinery relocations will disturb routine cost control. Management may wish to ask: "Recognizing that higher sales and profits will greatly improve the financial picture, what would be the effect of a short term business turndown of five percent in sales which forced a 4 percent reduction in prices concurrent with the addition of $400,000 in fixed costs and a two percent loss in variable cost control?"

The results would be a reduction in gross profits from $2,550,000 to $450,000 as calculated in Figure 10-7.

Timing of expenditures for expansion is important for maintaining a healthy cash and profit picture. Idle capacity can seriously affect performance. Often, profits are made on the last ten percent of sales or production.

Analysis of these types are essential for an analytical approach to management judgment. In this age, it is ridiculous to move into the future on a hunch, hearsay, or experience.

Product Mix Change

The standard cost and target selling prices are based on normal volume and product mix. Should sales result in a shift of the product mix to one with a different contribution relationship, actual profits can be substantially different from standard profits.

Figure 10-8 illustrates an example of a product mix change to lower contribution items. The standard profits indicate a change from $2,550,000 to $2,556,000. However, the product mix with a low contribution item (Product Number 901) has shifted significantly from the normal used for cost calculations. Calculated profit figures are no longer valid.

The real profit will be:

Contribution	$5,678,000
Fixed Cost	$4,250,000
Profit	$1,428,000

PRODUCT NUMBER	CHANNEL OF DISTRIBUTION	SY PER YEAR (000)	NET TARGET SELLING PRICE	NET FORECASTED SELLING PRICE	TOTAL STANDARD COST	TOTAL VARIABLE COST*	CONTRIBUTION PER YARD	CONTRIBUTION PER YEAR ($000)	PROFIT PER YARD	PROFIT PER YEAR ($000)
101	RETAIL	1,000	3.38		2.78	2.33	$ 1.05	$1050	$ 0.60	$ 600
	LARGE VOLUME	200	3.17		2.59	2.30	0.87	174	0.58	116
201	RETAIL	2,000	3.48		3.10	2.45	1.03	2060	0.38	760
	LARGE VOLUME	400	3.18		2.81	2.39	0.79	316	0.36	144
301	RETAIL		4.32		3.90	3.31				
	LARGE VOLUME		4.04		3.65	3.28				
401	RETAIL	500	3.42		2.78	2.36	1.06	530	0.64	320
	LARGE VOLUME		3.26		2.64	2.33				
601	RETAIL		3.48		3.00	2.54				
	LARGE VOLUME		3.17		2.80	2.51				
701	RETAIL		4.00		3.50	2.98				
	LARGE VOLUME		3.67		3.27	2.95				
801	RETAIL		4.05		3.62	3.05				
	LARGE VOLUME		3.78		3.38	3.03				
901	RETAIL	2,000	2.72		2.46	2.05	0.67	1340	0.26	520
	LARGE VOLUME	400	2.54		2.30	2.02	0.52	208	0.24	96
TOTAL		6,500						$5678 4250		$2556
						FIXED COST		$1428		

* INCLUDING OFF-QUALITY, CLAIMS, + RETURNS

FIGURE 10-8
PROFIT FORECAST—PRODUCT MIX CHANGE

PRODUCT NUMBER	CHANNEL OF DISTRIBUTION	SY PER YEAR (000)	NET TARGET SELLING PRICE	NET FORECASTED SELLING PRICE	TOTAL STANDARD COST	TOTAL VARIABLE COST*	CONTRIBUTION PER YARD	CONTRIBUTION PER YEAR ($000)	PROFIT PER YARD	PROFIT PER YEAR ($000)
1C1	RETAIL	600	3.38		2.78	2.33	$ 1.05	$ 630	$ 0.60	$ 360
	LARGE VOLUME	600	3.17		2.59	2.30	0.87	522	0.58	348
2C1	RETAIL	1200	3.48		3.10	2.45	1.03	1236	0.38	456
	LARGE VOLUME	1200	3.18		2.81	2.39	0.79	948	0.36	432
3C1	RETAIL		4.32		3.90	3.31				
	LARGE VOLUME		4.04		3.65	3.28				
4C1	RETAIL	200	3.42		2.78	2.36	1.06	212	0.64	128
	LARGE VOLUME	300	3.26		2.64	2.33	0.93	279	0.62	186
6C1	RETAIL		3.48		3.00	2.54				
	LARGE VOLUME		3.17		2.80	2.51				
7C1	RETAIL		4.00		3.50	2.98				
	LARGE VOLUME		3.67		3.27	2.95				
8C1	RETAIL		4.05		3.62	3.05				
	LARGE VOLUME		3.78		3.38	3.03				
9C1	RETAIL	1200	2.72		2.46	2.05	0.67	804	0.26	312
	LARGE VOLUME	1200	2.54		2.30	2.02	0.52	624	0.24	288
TOTAL		6500						$5255		$2510
							FIXED COST	4250		
								$1005		

* INCLUDING OFF-QUALITY, CLAIMS, + RETURNS

FIGURE 10-9

PROFIT FORECAST—CHANNEL OF DISTRIBUTION CHANGE

It is in these situations that contribution is the only valid basis for forecasting profits.

Channel of Distribution Change

In addition to the product mix changes, a substantial distortion of contribution to profits can occur by a shift in the volume through the respective channels of distribution.

Figure 10-9 indicates a further shift from the product mix into a heavier large proportion of large volume channel of distribution sales.

Standard profit calculations indicate a profit of $2,510,000. However, contribution analysis indicates that the real profit will be:

Contribution	$5,255,000
Fixed Cost	4,250,000
Profit	$1,005,000

These two analyses combined indicate that a shift in the product mix will reduce profits from $2,550,000 to $1,428,000. The shift in channel of distribution will reduce profits to $1,005,000.

Managers must constantly monitor their normal versus actual product mix and channel of distribution sales patterns in order to insure that sales are not shifting into lower contribution products or channels of distribution with a lower return.

Other Profit Forecast

The data accumulated using the methods described herein can be utilized for the specific analysis of customers, products, territories, or other sub-divisions which may be required.

PRODUCT NUMBER	CUSTOMER	SY PER YEAR (000)	NET TARGET SELLING PRICE	TOTAL DOLLAR SALES	TOTAL STANDARD COST	TOTAL VARIABLE COST*	CONTRIBUTION PER YARD	CONTRIBUTION PER YEAR ($000)	PROFIT PER YARD	PROFIT PER YEAR ($000)
901	CUSTOMER A	200	2.72	$ 544	2.46	2.05	0.67	$ 134	0.26	$ 52
	TOTAL: CUSTOMER A			$ 544				$ 134		$ 52
701	CUSTOMER B	100	4.00	$ 400	3.50	2.98	1.02	$ 102	0.50	$ 50
801	CUSTOMER B	100	4.05	405	3.62	3.05	1.00	100	0.43	43
	TOTAL: CUSTOMER B			$ 805				$ 202		$ 93

* INCLUDING OFF-QUALITY + CLAIMS

FIGURE 10-10
PROFIT FORECAST—CUSTOMER ANALYSIS

Figure 10-10 illustrates an example of a typical customer analysis. In this example, both Customer A and Customer B are buying 200,000 units per year. However, Customer B is contributing substantially more to sales and profits than Customer A.

Sales analysis of this type should be based on actual selling prices in order to get the true worth of an individual customer, territory, or salesman as shown in Figure 10-11. Where the net target selling price is used, it must be adjusted to actual selling prices by a price variance.

In most situations analyzed, a few customers or products are contributing significantly to financial results. Sometimes, a majority of the customers are buying at the reduced prices, high volume of discontinued merchandise, off-quality products, or low contribution items. Often, many customers *cause cost* rather than *improve performance*.

The actual dropping of sales potential or elimination of a customer which does not contribute is a trying decision for managers. Yet, effective management must face up to the hard facts and take action to eliminate those customers, products, or divisions which are *causing* costs rather than contributing significantly to financial results.

Much attention is given to the development and introduction of new products, and this is essential. The life cycle of products is constantly being shortened. Often, it is the failure to drop old products, styles, and colors which lead to poor financial results.

People and Communications

Many times, our most important resource, people, spend most of their time on trivial problems rather than those which will produce constructive and lasting results consistent with management's objective. Sometimes, our engineers will work on *interesting* rather than useful products. A key problem with people during the growth in size and centralization of the business establishment is the motivation of individual responsibility and initiative, in the face of necessity for conformance with standard policies and procedures. Even with automation and centralization, the big decisions still have to do with people.

Managers must assign a priority to motivating or providing people the opportunity to take maximum advantage of their individual potential. This may require a rethinking of past performance and the division of labor into its simplest and most repetitive elements. It may be better not to direct jobs into molds requiring identical skills and methods. Instead, jobs requiring every person to use his specific talents may be required.

Managers must continually seek out the reason for lack of effectiveness for obtaining maximum potential from people. The fact is, the term "labor cost" should be eliminated and replaced by the term "personnel cost". A satisfactory personnel situation today may be unsatisfactory tomorrow. The needs of people are continually changing and management's doors must be open to this change. Almost every person wants to do a good job and make a constructive contribution to the firm's business success. Managers must provide the opportunity. Improvements do not occur by chance. They must be planned and managed.

Managers must take action—that of determining what products, what activities, and what cost centers do not contribute to effective results. It is not the cost of wrong

EUROPEAN CARPET COMPANY
PROFIT CONTROL STATEMENT
SALESMAN A

| | | THIS MONTH | | | YEAR-TO-DATE | |
	STANDARD	ACTUAL	VARIANCE	STANDARD	ACTUAL	VARIANCE
GROSS DOLLARS	$100,000	$90,000	($10,000)			
TERMS	5,000	4,000	+ 1,000			
DISCOUNTS	1,000	2,000	(1,000)			
CLAIMS/RETURNS	1,000	1,000	-			
NET DOLLARS	$ 93,000	$83,000	($10,000)			
VARIABLE COSTS						
MANUFACTURING	$ 63,000	$59,000	$ 4,000			
DISTRIBUTION	5,000	4,000	1,000			
SALES	2,000	1,800	200			
TOTAL:						
VARIABLE COSTS	$ 70,000	$64,800	$ 5,200			
CONTRIBUTION	$23,000	$18,200	($ 4,800)			
VARIANCES						
PRICE	($ 2,000)					
VOLUME	(3,300)					
OFF-QUALITY, ETC.	500					
TOTAL VARIANCES	($ 4,800)					
KEY RATIOS						
PRICE RATIO	0.98					
QUALITY RATIO	0.97					
VOLUME RATIO	0.90					
NEW CUSTOMERS	1.40					
NEW ITEM SALES	1.10					
TRAVEL EXPENSE	0.96					

FIGURE 10-11
SALESMAN ANALYSIS

decisions which give managers trouble; these show up in sales and profit analysis. It is often the uncalculated costs of indecision that leads to lack of effectiveness.

The key decision to effective management may simply be deciding what not to do with time and resources. A start may be to list all the resource and time demands on three pieces of paper. On one, list the "true and important" things which must be done now. On the second, list the "true and trivial" things which should be accomplished. On the last, list the "false and unimportant" demands. Then, throw away list two, issue "No" directives on number three and allocate the managers and firms' time and resources to obtaining positive action with a permanent solution to the items on list one.

The difference between an average company and a highly profitable one may be small, but the difference is all profit. In education, the difference between a grade of 92 and 96 is nothing—it is still an "A". In business, the difference between 92 and 96 can be $400, $400,000, or $4,000,000—all profit. Essentially, managers have available the same machinery and materials. The big difference is in management's ability to challenge and motivate people concurrently with developing a marketing orientation for the firm.

Effective results are obtained by an analytical approach to business judgment, through analysis of information, allocation of resources, decisions and action.

The first decision is establishing an objective and allocation of resources to obtain this objective. The important point is not how much a manager misses his target; the truly disturbing fact is not to have a target to miss.

There is another three-step method of obtaining results:

Determine where the business should be going,
Start in that direction, and
Keep on going.

Business horizons are truly unlimited. Yet, history repeats itself. Behind the great advances stand a few men willing to take risks, make decisions, and take action.

SUMMARY

Effective management requires control of the total business enterprise at all three levels—supervisors, managers, and executives.

A Management Control Statement for the executive level is displayed in this chapter. This includes management objective profits, reasons for variation, forecast of future conditions, and a comparison to prior years' statistics.

Cash flow analysis and cash forecasting are discussed as well as profit forecasting and break-even analysis. Other examples explain how managers can use information to forecast the effects of reduced operations, increased operations, and other business situations. The change in financial results for product mix and channel of distribution variations are explained. Special consideration is given to customer analysis and control of salesmen.

This book is a guide to the developing of effective information for management decisions and actions. The first decision is to set an objective and strive to achieve this target through analysis of information, allocation of resources, and an analytical approach to business judgment.

Index